Open Court
Basic Readers

Publisher
M. Blouke Carus

General Manager
Howard R. Webber

Head, Editorial Department
Thomas G. Anderson

Associate Editor
Dale E. Howard

Editorial Assistant
Catherine E. Anderson

Administrative Assistants
June E. Hebel
Diane M. Sikora

A Trip Through Wonderland

Open Court Basic Readers

Editors:
Marianne Carus
Thomas G. Anderson
Howard R. Webber

Open Court Publishing Company
La Salle, Illinois 61301

Acknowledgments

FOR PERMISSION to reprint copyrighted material, grateful acknowledgment is made to the following publishers:

Appleton-Century-Crofts for "The Ox Who Won the Forfeit" from *Jataka Tales* by Ellen C. Babbitt. Copyright 1912, by the Century Company. Reprinted by permission of the publishers Appleton-Century, an affiliate of Meredith Press.

E. P. Dutton & Co. for "Tracks in the Snow," copyright 1941, by Marchette Chute. From the book *Around and About* by Marchette Chute. Published in 1957 by E. P. Dutton & Co., Inc., and reprinted with their permission.

Harper & Row, Publishers, Inc. for "Otto" from *Bronzeville Boys and Girls* by Gwendolyn Brooks, copyright © 1956 by Gwendolyn Brooks Blakely.

Holt, Rinehart and Winston, Inc. for "The Elephant's Trunk" from *A Rocket in My Pocket,* compiled by Carl Withers. Copyright 1948 by Carl Withers. Reprinted by permission of Holt, Rinehart and Winston, Inc.

Houghton Mifflin Company for "Why the Bear Has a Short Tail" from *The Book of Nature Myths* by Florence Holbrook, copyright 1930; and "The Dog Gellert" from *The Book of Legends* by Horace E. Scudder.

J. B. Lippincott Company for "Giacco and His Bean" from *Picture Tales from the Italian* by Florence Botsford. Copyright 1929 by Florence Botsford; copyright renewed 1957 by Rosamond Marshall. Published by J. B. Lippincott Company.

McGraw-Hill Book Company for "Sam" from *Sam* by Ann Herbert Scott, drawings by Symeon Shimin. Copyright © 1967 by Ann Herbert Scott & Symeon Shimin.

Isaac Bashevis Singer for "A Parakeet Named Dreidel" by Isaac Bashevis Singer, copyright © 1975, 1976 by Isaac Bashevis Singer. "A Parakeet Named Dreidel" was first published, in slightly different form, in *Cricket* magazine.

Frederick Warne & Co., Ltd. for "The Tale of Peter Rabbit" and illustrations by Beatrix Potter, reproduced by permission of the publisher, Frederick Warne & Co., Ltd.

All possible care has been taken to trace ownership and obtain permission for each selection included. If any errors or omissions have occurred, they will be corrected in subsequent editions, provided they are brought to the publisher's attention.

Contents

Part One: Stories and Poems Everyone Likes

Part Two: Folk Tales from Many Lands

Part Three: Fables and Folk Tales

Part Four: For Readers Brave and Bold

Part Five: On Your Own

THE ILLUSTRATIONS of the following artists appear on the pages indicated in parentheses.

Enrico Arno (15, 74, 75, 120, 142), Melanie Arwin (7, 24, 40-43, 64-67, 92, 98, 115, 116, 124), Idelette Bordigoni (108, 110, 148, 150), Cary (25, 137, 140, 141), Eva Cellini (36, 37), Joseph Cellini (2, 3, 83, 89), Currier and Ives (86), Mike Eagle (35, 111, 122, 123), Imero Gobatto (20, 23, 152), Marylin Hafner (Covers), Trina Schart Hyman/Lydia Dabcovitch (51, 52), Trina Schart Hyman (54, 78, 81, 128, 130-132), Robin Jacques (27, 157), Randy Jones (103, 105), Fen Lasell (45, 59, 61), W.T. Mars (29), Barbara McClintock (32, 72, 112), Beatrix Potter (9-14), Symeon Shimin (165-183), Su Zan Noguchi Swain (5, 69, 76, 158, 161), Lorna Tomei (17, 56, 85), Mary Winifred Walter (63, 94, 106, 114, 134, 135, 144, 162), Alessandra Zucchelli (31). Design: John Grandits

Part One
Stories and Poems Everyone Likes

A book is a pleasure;
A book is a treasure;
A book means much to me.

A book is a joy
To a girl or a boy
As only a book can be.

The Camel's Nose

Old Fable

One cold night an Arab was sitting inside his tent. Suddenly a camel stuck his nose under the flap of the tent and said, "Master, be good enough to let me put my head inside the tent, for it is cold outside."

"Very well," said the Arab, "you may put your head inside my tent."

So the camel put his head into the tent. Then in a little while the camel said, "Good master, pray let me put my neck in the tent also. I may catch cold if my head is warm and my neck is cold."

"Very well," replied the Arab, "you may put your neck in the tent, too."

After a little while the camel said again, "Kind master, allow me to put my forelegs in the tent. They take up only a little room, and it is uncomfortable standing this way."

"Very well," said the Arab, "you may do so." The Arab moved over to make room for the camel, for the tent was very small.

Then in a little while the camel said, "Generous master, permit me to stand all the way in the tent. I keep the flap of the tent open standing this way, and the cold air rushes inside."

"Very well, then," said the Arab. "You may come all the way inside."

The camel crowded his way into the tent, but the tent was too small for both.

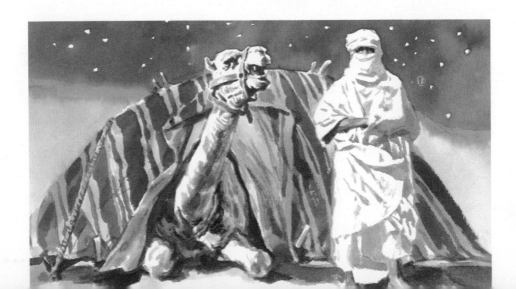

"I think that there is not room for both of us in the tent," said the camel. "Since you are smaller than I, it would be better if you stood outside."

With these words the camel gave the Arab a little push. Soon the Arab found himself standing outside in the cold, while the camel was enjoying the warmth of the tent.

As the Arab stood shivering from the cold, he said to himself, "I can see now that it is better to stop bad things before they get started."

QUESTIONS

1. Why do you think this story is called *The Camel's Nose*?
2. What reasons did the camel give for wanting to come farther into the tent each time? Do they seem like good reasons?
3. What did the Arab learn from his adventure with the camel?
4. Can you think of other bad things which should be stopped before they get started?

Say Well and Do Well

Anonymous

Say well and do well
  End with one letter;
Say well is good,
  Do well is better.

The Ants and the Grasshopper

Aesop

Once a family of ants lived on a hillside. They were very busy ants. They took good care of the baby ants, and they stored up food for the winter.

In a field nearby lived a grasshopper. He did not work. All day long he danced and sang. When he saw the ants hard at work, he said, "Why do you work so hard?"

"We must work," said the ants. "We must get ready for winter. We cannot find food then."

WORDS TO WATCH

stored	gathering	grasshopper
ready	through	covered

"I have never been hungry yet," said the grasshopper.

"You will be hungry when winter comes," said the ants.

"Winter is a long way off," said the grasshopper. Then he danced away.

"That grasshopper will be sorry when it is too late," said the ants.

By and by winter came. How cold the mornings were! The long grass was stiff with frost. The birds had gone away to their winter homes. The ants ran into their house and shut the door. It was warm in their house.

But where was the grasshopper? He had no home, and he could find nothing to eat. The ground was covered with snow. His legs were stiff with cold. He could not dance any more, and he did not feel like singing. He went to the ants' house.

"Please give me some food, dear ants," he said. "I am very hungry."

"But we have only enough food for ourselves," said the ants. "While we were working and gathering food, you were dancing and singing. Now see if your dancing and singing will get you through the winter."

And so the grasshopper was turned away. The ants never saw him again.

QUESTIONS
---

1. Why was the grasshopper hungry when winter came?
2. Do you feel sorry for the grasshopper? Why or why not?

The Squirrel

Anonymous

Whisky, frisky,
Hippity hop,
Up he goes
To the tree top!

Whirly, twirly,
Round and round,
Down he scampers
To the ground.

Furly, curly,
What a tail!
Tall as a feather,
Broad as a sail!

Where's his supper?
In the shell,
Snappity, crackity,
Out it fell!

Rhyming Words (All Kinds)

I. Read and Spell

bake	*flower*	*toe*	*girl*
rake	sour	go	curl
steak	tower	slow	twirl
make	shower	row	pearl
take	power	mow	whirl

clock	*tumble*	*thumb*	*fought*
block	rumble	some	bought
rock	stumble	dumb	taught
sock	fumble	crumb	caught
flock	mumble	come	brought

II. Read and Answer

1. Add more words to the lists in Part I.
2. Find three words that rhyme with each of these words:

    table   thing   school   drinking

III. Write

Write five sentences. In each sentence use two or three words that rhyme. Here is an example to help you: Dick threw the pie high in the sky.

The Tale of Peter Rabbit

Beatrix Potter

Once upon a time there were four little Rabbits, and their names were—Flopsy, Mopsy, Cotton-tail, and Peter.

They lived with their Mother in a sandbank, under the root of a very big fir tree.

"Now, my dears," said old Mrs. Rabbit one morning, "you may go into the fields or down the lane, but don't go into Mr. McGregor's garden. Your Father had an accident there: he was put in a pie by Mrs. McGregor. Now run along, and don't get into mischief. I am going out."

Then old Mrs. Rabbit took a basket and her umbrella and went through the wood to the baker's. She bought a loaf of brown bread and five currant buns.

Flopsy, Mopsy, and Cotton-tail, who were good little bunnies, went down the lane to gather blackberries, but Peter, who was very naughty, ran straight away to Mr. McGregor's garden and squeezed under the gate!

First he ate some lettuce and some French beans, and then he ate some radishes, and then feeling rather sick, he went to look for some parsley.

But around the end of a cucumber frame, whom should he meet but Mr. McGregor!

Mr. McGregor was on his hands and knees planting young cabbages, but he jumped up and ran after Peter, waving a rake and calling out, "Stop, thief!"

Peter was most dreadfully frightened; he rushed all over the garden, for he had forgotten the way back to the gate.

He lost one of his shoes among the cabbages and the other shoe among the potatoes.

After losing them, he ran on four legs and went faster, so that I think he might have got away altogether if he had not unfortunately run into a gooseberry net and got caught by the large buttons on his jacket. It was a blue jacket with brass buttons, quite new.

Peter gave himself up for lost and shed big tears, but his sobs were overheard by some friendly sparrows, who flew to him in great excitement and implored him to exert himself.

Mr. McGregor came up with a sieve, which he intended to pop upon the top of Peter, but Peter wriggled out just in time, leaving his jacket behind him, and rushed into the toolshed, and jumped into a can. It would have been a beautiful thing to hide in if it had not had so much water in it.

Mr. McGregor was quite sure that Peter was somewhere in the toolshed, perhaps hidden underneath a flowerpot. He began to turn them over carefully, looking under each one.

Presently Peter sneezed: "Kerty-schoo!" Mr. McGregor was after him in no time and tried to put his foot upon Peter, who jumped out the window, upsetting three plants. The window was too small for Mr. McGregor, and he was tired of running after Peter. He went back to work.

Peter sat down to rest; he was out of breath and trembling with fright, and he had not the least idea which way to go. Also he was very damp with sitting in the can.

After a time Peter began to wander about, going lippity—lippity—not very fast, and looking all around.

He found a door in a wall, but it was locked, and there was no room for a fat little rabbit to squeeze beneath.

An old mouse was running in and out over the stone doorstep, carrying peas and beans to her family in the wood. Peter asked her the way to the gate, but she had such a large pea in her mouth that she could not answer. She only shook her head at him. Peter began to cry.

Then he tried to find his way straight across the garden, but he became more and more puzzled. Presently he came to a pond where Mr. McGregor filled his water can. A white cat was staring at some goldfish; she sat very, very still, but now and then the tip of her tail twitched as if it were alive. Peter thought it best to go away without speaking to her; he had heard about cats from his cousin, little Benjamin Bunny.

He went back toward the toolshed, but suddenly, quite close to him, he heard the noise of a hoe—scr-r-ritch, scratch, scratch, scritch. Peter scuttered under the bushes. But presently, as nothing happened, he came out, and climbed upon a wheelbarrow, and peeped over. The first thing he saw was Mr. McGregor hoeing onions. His back was turned towards Peter, and beyond him was the gate!

Peter got down very quietly off the wheelbarrow and started running as fast as he could go, along a straight walk behind some black-currant bushes.

Mr. McGregor caught sight of him at the corner, but Peter did not care. He slipped under the gate, and was safe at last in the wood outside the garden.

Mr. McGregor hung up the little jacket and the shoes for a scarecrow to frighten the blackbirds.

Peter never stopped running or looked behind him till he got home to the big fir tree.

He was so tired that he flopped down upon the nice soft sand on the floor of the rabbit hole and shut his eyes. His mother was busy cooking; she wondered what he had done with his clothes. It was the second little jacket and pair of shoes that Peter had lost in a fortnight!

I am sorry to say that Peter was not very well during the evening.

His mother put him to bed and made some camomile tea, and she gave a dose of it to Peter!

"One tablespoonful to be taken at bedtime."

But Flopsy, Mopsy, and Cotton-tail had bread and milk and blackberries for supper.

THE BUNDLE OF STICKS

Aesop

A certain father had a family of sons, who were forever quarreling among themselves. No words he could say did the least good. He tried to think of a way to show them that quarreling would lead them to misfortunes.

One day the quarreling was much more violent than usual. Each of the sons became gloomy and cross. The father asked one of his sons to bring him a bundle of sticks. Then, handing the bundle to each of his sons in turn, he told them to try to break it. But although each one tried his best, none was able to do so.

The father then untied the bundle and gave the sticks to his sons to break one by one. This they did very easily.

"My sons," said the father, "do you not see how certain it is that if you agree with each other and help each other, it will be impossible for your enemies to injure you? But if you are divided among yourselves, you will be no stronger than a single stick in that bundle."

QUESTIONS

1. What were the sons doing among themselves?
2. What did the father want to do with the bundle of sticks? Why?
3. Why couldn't each son break the bundle of sticks?
4. Why could they break each stick one by one?
5. Explain the main point of this story.

Poor Old Lady

Mother Goose

oor old lady, she swallowed a fly.
don't know why she swallowed a fly.
oor old lady, I think she'll die.

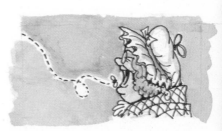

oor old lady, she swallowed a spider.
squirmed and wriggled and turned inside her.
he swallowed the spider to catch the fly.
don't know why she swallowed a fly.
oor old lady, I think she'll die.

oor old lady, she swallowed a bird.
ow absurd! She swallowed a bird.
he swallowed the bird to catch the spider.
he swallowed the spider to catch the fly.
don't know why she swallowed a fly.
oor old lady, I think she'll die.

oor old lady, she swallowed a cat.
hink of that! She swallowed a cat.

She swallowed the cat to catch the bird.
She swallowed the bird to catch the spider.
She swallowed the spider to catch the fly.
I don't know why she swallowed a fly.
Poor old lady, I think she'll die.

Poor old lady, she swallowed a dog.
She went the whole hog when she swallowed the dog.
She swallowed the dog to catch the cat.
She swallowed the cat to catch the bird.
She swallowed the bird to catch the spider.
She swallowed the spider to catch the fly.
I don't know why she swallowed a fly.
Poor old lady, I think she'll die.

Poor old lady, she swallowed a cow.
I don't know how she swallowed the cow.
She swallowed the cow to catch the dog.
She swallowed the dog to catch the cat.
She swallowed the cat to catch the bird.
She swallowed the bird to catch the spider.
She swallowed the spider to catch the fly.
I don't know why she swallowed a fly.
Poor old lady, I think she'll die.

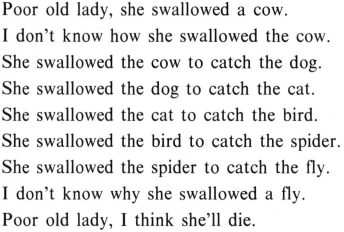

Poor old lady, she swallowed a horse.
She died, of course.

Flowers

I. Read and Pronounce

rose	tulip	larkspur
daisy	violet	snapdragon
daffodil	carnation	zinnia
lilac	petunia	lily
marigold	crocus	orchid
dahlia	forget-me-not	pansy
poppy	geranium	buttercup

II. Read and Answer

1. Which flowers in Part I appear very early in the spring?
2. Name some other flowers.
3. Which flowers have you seen?
4. Have you ever grown flowers?
5. What flower do you like best?
6. Why do you think people grow flowers?
7. How many words in Part I can you spell?

III. Write

1. Write five sentences. In each one, use a word from Part I.
2. Write a little story about some flowers in your garden or house.

GIACCO AND HIS BEAN

Italian Folk Tale

Once upon a time there was a little boy named Giacco, who had no father or mother. The only food he had was a cup of beans. Each day he ate a bean, until finally there was only one left. So he put this bean into his pocket and walked until night. He saw a little house under a mulberry tree. Giacco knocked at the door. An old man came out and asked what he wanted.

"I have no father or mother," said Giacco. "And I have no food except this one bean."

	WORDS TO WATCH	
Giacco	mulberry	knock
kennel	brute	disgusting
creature	worthless	majesty

20

"Poor boy," said the kind old man. He gave Giacco four mulberries to eat and let him sleep by the fire. During the night the bean rolled out of Giacco's pocket, and the cat ate it. When Giacco awoke, he cried, "Kind old man, your cat has eaten my bean. What shall I do?"

"You may take the cat," said the kind old man. "I do not want to keep such a wicked animal."

So Giacco took the cat and walked all day until he came to a little house under a walnut tree. He knocked at the door. An old man came out and asked what he wanted.

"I have no father or mother," said Giacco. "And I have only this cat that ate the bean."

"Too bad!" said the kind old man. He gave Giacco three walnuts to eat and let him sleep in the dog kennel. During the night the dog ate up the cat. When Giacco awoke, he cried, "Kind old man, your dog has eaten my cat!"

"You may take the dog," said the kind old man. "I do not want to keep such a mean brute."

So Giacco took the dog and walked all day until he came to a little house under a fig tree. He knocked at the door. An old man came out and asked what he wanted.

"I have no father or mother," said Giacco. "I have only this dog that ate the cat that ate the bean."

"How very sad!" said the kind old man. He gave Giacco two figs to eat and let him sleep in the pig sty.

That night the pig ate the dog. When Giacco awoke, he cried, "Kind old man, your pig has eaten my dog!"

"You may take the pig," said the kind old man. "I do not care to keep such a disgusting creature."

So Giacco took the pig and walked all day until he came to a little house under a chestnut tree. He knocked at the door. An old man came out and asked what he wanted.

"I have no father or mother and only this pig that ate the dog that ate the cat that ate the bean," said Giacco.

"How pitiful!" said the kind old man. He gave Giacco one chestnut to eat and let him sleep in the stable. During the night the horse ate the pig. When Giacco awoke, he cried, "Kind old man, your horse has eaten my pig!"

"You may take the horse," said the kind old man. "I do not want to keep such a worthless beast." So Giacco rode away on the horse.

He rode all day until he came to a castle. He knocked at the gate, and a voice cried, "Who is there?"

"It is Giacco. I have no father or mother, and I have only this horse that ate the pig that ate the dog that ate the cat that ate the bean."

"Ha! Ha! Ho! Ho!" laughed the king. "Whoever heard of a bean that ate the cat that ate the dog that ate the pig that ate the horse?"

"Excuse me, Your Majesty; it is just the other way around," said Giacco. "It was the horse that ate the pig that ate the dog that ate the cat that ate the bean."

"Ha! Ha! Ho! Ho!" laughed the king. "My mistake! Of course, it was the bean that ate the horse; no, I mean the

horse that ate the bean; no, I mean—Ha! Ha! Ho!
Ho!" laughed the king, and the knights began to laugh, and
the ladies began to laugh, and the maids began to laugh,
and the cooks began to laugh, and the bells began to ring, and
the birds began to sing, and all the people in the kingdom
laughed and sang.

The king came to the gate and said, "Giacco, if you will tell
me every day about the bean that ate the horse; I mean the
horse that ate the bean; no, I mean the horse that ate the pig
that ate the dog that ate the cat that ate the bean—Ha! Ha!
Ha! Ha! Ho! Ho! Ho! Ho!—you shall sit on the throne
beside me!"

So Giacco put on a golden crown and sat upon the throne,
and every day he told about the horse that ate the pig that ate
the dog that ate the cat that ate the bean, and everybody
laughed and sang and lived happily ever after.

Happiness
Anonymous

What are you thinking of, my pretty maid?
  "I'm thinking how happy I am," she said.
And what is your happiness, my pretty maid?
  "Oh, flowers, and summer, and sunshine," she said.
And what will you do, when the flowers are dead?
  "I'll try to be happy without them," she said.

QUESTIONS

1. Could you be happy without flowers and sunshine and summer? Why or why not?
2. What are the things that make you the happiest?

Starry Night

Anonymous

One summer evening Juanita and her little sister Rosa sat down on the grass to rest. It began to grow dark. One by one the stars came out. At last it was quite dark. The sky was dotted with bright stars.

Rosa watched the stars quietly for some time. Then she said, "Where are the stars in the daytime?"

"They are shining just as they are now," said Juanita.

"Are they always shining, day and night?" asked Rosa.

"Yes, they are like the sun; they shine all the time."

"Then why can't we see them during the day?"

"Because the sun gives much more light than the stars," said Juanita. "You know that if you turn the porch light on in the daytime, you can hardly see it. When we first sat down here, we could not see even one star. But then it grew dark enough to see the brightest stars. As it grew darker still, we saw other stars. If something should happen at noon to make it quite dark, then we could see the stars."

"How strange that seems!" said Rosa. "I did not know before that the stars were up in the sky in the daytime."

"Did you know that you can tell which way is north by looking at the stars?" said Juanita.

"How is that done?" asked Rosa.

"All you have to do is to find the North Star," said Juanita.

"Look where I am pointing. Do you see seven stars in a group? They seem to make the shape of a dipper. Four of these stars make the bowl of the Dipper. The other three bend away and make the handle. The two bright stars at the front of the bowl are called the Pointers. They point toward the North Star.

"The Dipper moves about, but these two stars always point to the North Star. People long ago thought that these stars made the shape of a bear, so they called this group the Big Bear.

"There is a Little Bear too. It looks like a little dipper to us. The North Star is at the end of this handle."

"Why should I know where the North Star is?" asked Rosa.

"Because you will be able to tell directions at night. If you're ever lost at night, that star tells you where north is. If

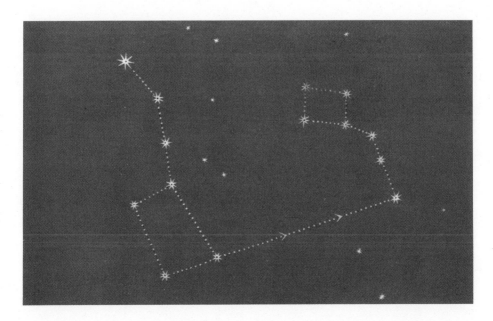

you know where north is and in which direction your house is, you can find your way home again."

"It is fun to lie here and study the stars," said Rosa.

"Yes," said Juanita. "And some people study about suns and stars and outer space all their lives. These people are called astronomers. It is very exciting to study about the sun and stars and outer space because there is so much to learn."

QUESTIONS

1. Why can't we see the stars in the daytime?
2. How can you find the North Star?
3. How many stars are in the Big Dipper?
4. What is another name for the Big Dipper and the Little Dipper?
5. On the next clear night, see if you can find the North Star, the Big Dipper, and the Little Dipper.

Numbers (10 to 100)

I. Read and Spell

eleven	seventeen	fifty
twelve	eighteen	sixty
thirteen	nineteen	seventy
fourteen	twenty	eighty
fifteen	thirty	ninety
sixteen	forty	one hundred

II. Read

twenty-four	sixty-one	thirty-one
thirty-six	eighty-nine	twenty-six
seventy-five	ninety-three	forty-nine
forty-five	fifty-two	seventy-eight

III. Write

Write the words for these numbers:

17	27	18
20	56	69
34	100	42

A Story of a Turnip

Old Folk Tale

One day a poor farmer found a large turnip in his garden.

"I will take this turnip to the king," he said, "and offer it to him as a gift. He is always glad when we have good crops in our gardens and fields."

So the farmer carried the turnip to the castle. The king took it and admired its great size and beauty. Then he said some kind words to the poor man and gave him three gold pieces.

Near the village where the poor farmer lived was another farmer. He was very rich, and he always wanted to be richer. He heard about the kindness which the king had shown to the poor farmer and about the money he had given him.

"I have a big calf," said he, "the largest and finest calf in the country. I will take it to the king and offer it as a gift. If

---

WORDS TO WATCH

brought   offering   calf

he gave three gold pieces for a turnip, how much more will he give for a beautiful calf!"

So he tied a rope around the calf's neck and led it to the castle.

"My good king," he said, "here is a calf which I have fed and brought up with great care. I want to show my love for you by offering it to you as a gift. Please take it with my best wishes."

But the king understood what was in the mind of the farmer, and he said that he did not want the calf. The man begged the king very hard to take the gift. He would never be happy, he said, if he should have to take the calf back home.

"Very well," said the wise king, "since you wish me to do so, I will take it. And in order that you may know how well I think of you, I will give you a present which cost me at least three times as much as your calf is worth."

Saying these words, he gave the farmer the big turnip which had led to this gift-making. And the farmer, as he went sadly home, thought to himself that he had done a very foolish thing.

QUESTIONS

1. Why did the poor farmer give the king a turnip?
2. Why did the rich farmer give the king a calf?
3. Why didn't the king want to take the calf?

A Bird Came Down the Walk

Emily Dickinson

A bird came down the walk:
He did not know I saw,
He bit an angle-worm in halves
And ate the fellow, raw.

And then he drank a dew
From a convenient grass,
And then hopped sidewise to the wall
To let a beetle pass.

QUESTIONS

1. What did the bird do when he saw the angle-worm?
2. What did he do when he saw the beetle?
3. Why do you think he did not do the same thing to both the worm and the beetle?

The Happy Robin and the Gloomy Raven

Fidelia Bridges

One morning in the early spring a raven was sitting on one of the branches of an old oak tree. He felt very ugly and cross and could only say, "Ugh! Ugh!"

Soon a little robin flew into the same tree. She was looking for a place to build her nest. "Good morning," she said to the raven in a cheery voice.

But the raven did not answer; he only looked at the clouds and muttered something about the cold wind.

WORDS TO WATCH		
raven	muttered	complaining

32

"I said good morning to you," said the robin as she hopped from branch to branch.

"You seem very merry this morning about nothing," said the raven.

"Why shouldn't I be merry?" said the robin. "Spring has come, and everybody should be glad and happy."

"I am not happy," said the raven. "Don't you see those black clouds above us? It is going to snow."

"Very well," answered the robin, "but I shall keep on singing until the snow comes. A merry song will not make the weather any colder."

"You are very silly," said the raven.

The robin flew to another tree and kept on singing, but the raven sat still and made himself very unhappy. "The wind is cold and it always blows the wrong way for me," said he.

Soon the sun came out warm and bright, and the clouds went away. But the raven was as sad as ever.

The grass began to spring up in the meadows. Green leaves and flowers were seen in the woods. Birds and bees flew here and there in the glad sunshine. But the raven just sat on the branch of the old oak.

"It is always too warm or too cold," he said. "True, it is just right now, but I know that the sun will soon shine hot enough to burn me up. Then, tomorrow, it will be colder than ever before. I do not see how anyone can sing at a time like this."

The robin came back to the tree carrying a straw in her mouth. "Well, my friend," said the robin, "where is your snow?"

"Don't say anything," replied the raven. "It will snow all the harder because of this sunshine."

"Snow or sunshine," said the robin, "you will always be complaining. I think it is better to look on the bright side of everything. I have a song for every day in the year."

QUESTIONS

1. Why wasn't the raven happy?
2. Why was the robin happy?
3. When the weather is gloomy or sunny, is it better to be more like the raven or the robin? Why?

Birdwatching

Arther S. Trace, Jr.

Do you know what a birdwatcher is? Of course, you do. A birdwatcher watches birds. If you have sharp eyes, you can be one too!

If you watch birds on the way to school or to the library or even in your own yard, you can learn much about the world of birds. You will have a lot of fun too.

In the springtime you may see a baby robin learning to fly. You will know it is a baby robin because he wears a spotted vest.

WORDS TO WATCH			
library	accusing	search	hummingbird
woodpecker	soaring	guard	fiery
chickadee	suet	penguin	ostrich

You may see a blue jay stealing an egg from the nest of a smaller bird. His cry sounds like "Thief! Thief!" as if he were accusing some other bird of stealing the egg. Blue jays may not be very nice, but they are pretty.

You may see or hear a red-headed woodpecker drilling holes in a tree or telephone pole in search of a bug breakfast.

If you are lucky, you may even see a hummingbird as he flits from flower to flower. He is the smallest of all the birds. He is the only bird that can fly backwards, and he can move his wings so fast that you cannot see them.

Once you see a cardinal, you will never forget him. He is fiery red all over and wears a fine red crest on his head. He has a song as gay as can be when he sings "what-cheer, what-cheer." The female cardinal has brown feathers and is not nearly so brightly colored. She is harder to find.

If you go for a walk in the country, you may see and hear many birds that you do not often see in the city. You may see a hawk soaring high in the sky as he searches the earth below for a dinner of fresh mice or tender chicken.

You may see an owl sleeping high in a tree and waiting for night to come because he doesn't like the daylight.

Or you may see a lone crow perched on the branch of a tall tree. She may be a guard on the lookout for Farmer Brown, for she often has crow friends feasting in the cornfield. If you hear her cry, "Caw! Caw! Caw!" it may be that she sees Farmer Brown coming and is signaling her fellow corn stealers to fly to safety.

When it gets cold in the winter, many of the birds fly south to warmer weather. But if you take a walk in the woods in the wintertime, you can see many birds that did not fly south. You can see sparrows everywhere. They are used to snow and

cold weather. You may also see some playful chickadees. Chickadees like cold weather too, and you may hear one chirping gaily "Chick-a-dee-dee-dee," or see one eating upside down in a tree branch. If you have a piece of suet for him, he might even come down and take it from your fingers.

If you want to see an ostrich or a penguin, you will probably have to go to the zoo. But there are enough birds all about us in the fields and woods to give birdwatchers a lifetime of fun.

QUESTIONS

1. Which birds does "Birdwatching" tell about? What does it tell about them?
2. What kind of bird would you best like to watch? Why?
3. Be a birdwatcher after school or on the way to school in the morning and tell the class about the birds you saw and what they were doing.

Birds

I. Read and Spell

robin	cardinal	ostrich
sparrow	hummingbird	owl
bluebird	penguin	eagle
hawk	woodpecker	crow
parrot	duck	swan
goose	pigeon	peacock
canary	parakeet	stork

II. Read and Answer

1. Which of these birds is the largest? The smallest?
2. Which of these birds have you seen? Heard?
3. Which birds make good pets?
4. Which birds can be taught to talk?
5. Which birds cannot fly?
6. Which birds will eat small animals?
7. Which birds can you see only at the zoo?
8. Name some other birds.

III. Write

1. Write five sentences. In each one, use a word from Part I.
2. Write a little story about your favorite kind of bird.

Norma the Caterpillar

Joan Elma Rahn

One hot summer day, Ann helped her mother pull weeds between the tomato plants in their vegetable garden.

"There's a big green worm!" she cried.

"No, it's a caterpillar," said her mother. "After a moth lays eggs, each egg hatches into a larva that looks a little like a worm. Many insects produce larvae, but we call the larva of moths and butterflies a caterpillar.

"We must look to see if there are more of them and pick them. If we don't, they will harm the tomato plants."

WORDS TO WATCH		
vegetable	pupa	proboscis
larva	abdomen	nectar
cocoons	antennae	pollen

40

They looked a long time and found only a few caterpillars, for the caterpillars hid under the leaves. Ann's mother let one caterpillar stay on the plants so that Ann could watch it every day.

"I think I'll call her Norma," said Ann.

Ann held Norma in her hand. Along Norma's sides were several spots and some white lines, but mostly she was about the same shade of green as the tomato plant leaves. Her color protected her from birds that would like to catch and eat her. Ann put her back on a leaf. Norma moved under the leaf and began to eat it.

Ann went to the garden every day. Norma seemed to be getting bigger each time Ann saw her. That was not surprising, because Norma spent most of her time eating. She had strong jaws with which she bit off pieces of leaf and chewed them.

One day Ann found another caterpillar. It was covered by tiny white bumps. A wasp had laid her eggs in this caterpillar, and the eggs had grown into larvae that used the caterpillar as their food. Now they had changed into cocoons that looked like grains of puffed rice. Every day this caterpillar grew weaker. He did not move around as much as Norma did. He ate very little. Soon he would die. The wasp did not know it, but she had helped Ann's mother, for if there were too many caterpillars, they might eat all the tomato plants.

No wasp laid any eggs in Norma, however. No birds caught her either. She just continued to eat and grow.

Then one day in autumn, Norma burrowed into the ground. Here she became a hard, dry, brown pupa. As a pupa, Norma lay still. She did not eat. She looked dead. But Norma was alive. Slowly her body changed into a moth. She was no longer Norma the caterpillar, but Norma the hawkmoth.

In spring, Norma came out of the ground. She had four large, brown wings with beautiful markings. There were five orange spots on either side of her abdomen. On her head were two long antennae. Her mouth was different, too. Instead of having strong jaws that chewed leaves, Norma had a long, hollow proboscis. She used it to sip nectar from flowers just as you drink through a straw. When she wasn't using her proboscis, she rolled it up under her head.

Norma ate mostly at dusk. In the dim light it was difficult to see her, but every evening Norma flew from flower to flower. At each flower, a little pollen stuck to her body. At the next flower, some of the pollen brushed off her and landed on the flower. Then she picked up more pollen. In this way, without even knowing that she was doing it, Norma carried pollen from flower to flower. This helped the flowers to get seed. Next year, these seeds would grow into new plants, and they would provide nectar for more hawkmoths.

That spring, Ann's mother planted more tomato plants in her garden. One evening Norma visited them, but she did not come to eat. She laid eggs on the lower side of a leaf. They were greenish in color, almost like the color of the leaves. No one saw them hidden there.

In about a week, small caterpillars hatched out of the eggs. They looked the same as Norma had looked when Ann first found her.

Norma grew old, and one day she died. But every year there will be more caterpillars and more hawkmoths like her.

QUESTIONS

1. What are the four stages in the life of a moth?
2. Why does Norma's color as a caterpillar protect her from birds?
3. How does a caterpillar's life differ from that of a moth?

44

The Dog Gellert

Welsh Tale

In the mountains of Wales there was once a king who lived in a fine castle. The king had a little son whom he loved very dearly.

The servants loved the little boy very much, too. But his closest friend and playmate was his dog, whose name was Gellert. Gellert was a large and powerful hound. The king kept him there to protect his son from the wolves and other wild beasts that lived in the forest near the castle.

WORDS TO WATCH			
slain	Wales	Gellert	monument
protect	horrified	faithless	powerful
sword	shaggy	grave	approached
guardian	perhaps		

The king trusted the dog completely. One day when he went hunting, he told Gellert to stay home and take care of his little master. So Gellert lay down beside the little boy's bed and stretched his huge paws out as if to say, "No one shall come near my little master."

Late in the afternoon when the hunt was over, the king returned to his castle. As he approached the gate, Gellert bounded out to meet him. But the king was horrified to see blood around Gellert's mouth and on his body.

"O faithless hound!" he cried. "Is this the way you guard your little master?" And he drew his sword and with one blow laid the hound dead at his feet. Then he rushed into the castle and into his little son's room. The little boy's bed was empty, and clothes were thrown all about.

The king was terrified. Suddenly he heard a sound. Perhaps his son still lived. He went to the bed, and there behind it was his little boy, laughing and pulling the hair of a great shaggy wolf that lay dead beside him.

Then the king understood everything. The wolf had come in through the open door and had approached the little boy's bed. Gellert had sprung upon the wolf, fought with him, and slain him.

O happy father! To have his child back again! Oh unhappy king! To have slain the child's faithful guardian! He could not bring Gellert back to life, but he dug his grave and built about it a beautiful monument, which still stands today.

Dogs

I. Read and Pronounce

fox terrier	Great Dane	Chihuahua
poodle	Scottish terrier	Pekingese
English bulldog	collie	pointer
cocker spaniel	Saint Bernard	dachshund
mongrel	German shepherd	Old English sheepdog
Dalmatian	Alaskan husky	Boston terrier

II. Read and Answer

1. Which of these is the largest dog?
2. Which is the smallest?
3. Which dogs are the most useful to people? What do they do?
4. Tell what each of these dogs looks like.
5. Name some other kinds of dogs.
6. What kind of dog do you like best? Why?

III. Write

1. Write: A dog is a man's best friend.
2. Write five sentences, each one telling something about a kind of dog.
3. Write about your dog or about a dog you know.

I. A. You have read these stories in Part One of your book. Tell what each one is about.

> The Camel's Nose
>
> The Ants and the Grasshopper
>
> The Tale of Peter Rabbit
>
> The Bundle of Sticks
>
> Giacco and His Bean
>
> A Starry Night
>
> A Story of a Turnip
>
> The Happy Robin and the Gloomy Raven
>
> Birdwatching
>
> Norma the Caterpillar
>
> The Dog Gellert

   B. Which of these stories did you like best? Why?

II. A. Memorize a poem you read in Part One of your book and recite it to the class.

   B. Copy the poem you like best in Part One. Copy it carefully.

Part Two
Folk Tales from Many Lands

I'm glad the sky is painted blue
And the earth is painted green,
With such a lot of nice fresh air
All sandwiched in between.

A Parakeet Named Dreidel

Isaac B. Singer

It happened on Chanukkah about ten years ago. All day long a heavy snow was falling. Towards evening the sky cleared and a few stars appeared. A frost set in. The snow on the street sparkled like diamonds. It was the eighth day of Chanukkah, and my silver Chanukkah lamp stood on the window sill with eight candles burning. It was mirrored in the windowpane, and I imagined another lamp outside.

My wife Esther was frying potato pancakes, which are a Chanukkah treat. I sat with my son David at a table and played Dreidel with him. Suddenly David cried out: "Papa, look!" And he pointed to the window.

I looked up. I could hardly believe what I saw! Outside on the window sill stood a yellow-green bird watching the Chanukkah candles. In a moment I understood what had happened. A parakeet had escaped from its home. It had flown out into the cold street and had landed on my window sill, perhaps attracted by the light.

WORDS TO WATCH

Chanukkah	Dreidel	ceiling
windowpane	parakeet	miracle
Yiddish	attracted	millet
advertised	notice	elevator
		festival

50

A parakeet comes from warmer countries. It cannot stand the cold and frost for very long. At once I set out to save the bird from freezing. First I carried away the Chanukkah lamp so that the bird should not burn itself when it came in. Then I opened the window and with a quick wave of my hand shooed the parakeet inside. The whole thing took only a few seconds.

In the beginning the frightened bird flew from wall to wall. It hit itself against the ceiling. David tried to calm it. "Don't be afraid, little bird, we are your friends." Presently the bird flew towards David and landed on his head, as though it had been trained and was used to people. David began to dance and laugh from joy. My wife in the kitchen heard the noise and came out to see what had happened. When she saw the bird on David's head, she asked: "Where did you get a bird all of a sudden?"

"Mama, it just came to our window."

"To the window in the middle of winter?"

"Papa saved its life. It's a Chanukkah miracle!"

Soon the bird was not afraid of us. David lifted his hand to his forehead, and the bird settled on his finger. Esther placed a saucer of millet and a dish with water on the table, and the parakeet ate and drank. Then it saw the dreidel and began to push it with its beak. David exclaimed: "Look, the bird plays Dreidel."

David soon began to talk about buying a cage for the bird and also about giving it a name. Esther and I reminded him that the bird was not ours. We would try to find the owners, who probably missed the parakeet and worried about what had happened to it in the icy weather. David said, "Meanwhile, let's call it Dreidel."

That night Dreidel slept on a picture frame. In the morning it woke us with its singing and talking in Yiddish. We were filled with wonder and delight to hear a tiny parakeet talk!

The next day I posted a notice in the elevators of the neighborhood houses. It said that we had found a Yiddish-speaking parakeet. When a few days passed and no one called, I advertised in the newspaper for which I wrote. A week went by and no one claimed the bird. Only then did Dreidel become ours. We bought a large cage with all the toys that a bird might want. Because Chanukkah is a festival of freedom, we decided never to lock the cage. Dreidel was free to fly around the house whenever *he* pleased. (The man at the pet shop had told us that the bird was male.)

Dreidel is still with us, always eager to learn new words and new games. On Chanukkah he always gets a gift—a mirror, a ladder, a bathtub, a swing, or a jingle-bell. He even likes potato pancakes, as a parakeet named Dreidel should.

QUESTIONS

1. In what three ways is the family in this story celebrating Chanukkah?
2. Why did David name the parakeet "Dreidel"?
3. Find out more about the Chanukkah festival.

Who Has Seen the Wind?

Christina Rossetti

Who has seen the wind?
　Neither I nor you:
But when the leaves hang trembling,
　The wind is passing through.

Who has seen the wind?
　Neither you nor I:
But when the trees bow down their heads,
　The wind is passing by.

QUESTIONS

---

1. What are some of the other things that wind does besides shake the leaves and bend the trees?
2. Write or tell about when you like the wind and when you don't like it.

The Tale of the Clever Deer
Chinese Folk Tale

A little deer was quietly nibbling some grass, when suddenly a tiger jumped out of the bushes. At the sight of the fierce tiger, the little deer's heart stood still with fear. But since there was no way to escape, he bravely stood his ground.

Now, ordinarily, the tiger would have eaten so small and tender an animal. But this tiger had never seen a deer before.

"What are those things growing out of your head?" asked the tiger.

"Those are horns," said the little deer.

"Of what use are horns?" asked the tiger.

"Why, they are especially used to fork tigers," said the clever little deer.

"Really?" replied the tiger. "And what are all those white spots on your body for?"

"Don't you know?" said the little deer. "I thought everybody knew that. Every time I eat a tiger, a spot appears on my body. As you can see, I've eaten so many tigers that I'm practically covered with spots."

When the tiger heard this, he was so frightened that he bounded into the forest.

Pretty soon he met a fox. He told the fox of the fearsome animal he had just met—the animal who forked tigers with his horns and who had eaten so many tigers.

"A little deer forking and eating tigers!" laughed the fox. "Oh, what a trick he has played on you!"

The tiger couldn't believe that the little deer had fooled him so completely. But the fox said, "If you don't believe me, I'll show you myself. Just let me ride on your back and lead me to the deer. You'll soon see."

So they set out. When the little deer saw the tiger returning with the fox on his back, he knew at once that the fox had told the tiger the truth. He had to think fast to save himself, and think fast he did.

"Ho, there, friend fox!" he called. "I see you have kept your promise. You told me that you would bring a fine tiger for me to eat, and that surely is a beauty you're bringing me now!"

When the tiger heard this, he needed no more convincing. He darted back into the forest—with the fox in his mouth! And the clever little deer was saved!

QUESTIONS

---

1. What did the deer tell the tiger his horns and his spots were for?
2. Why did the deer have to think fast when he saw the tiger coming with the fox on his back?
3. Why did the tiger grab the fox in his mouth?

The Weather

I. Read and Spell

rain	rainbow	mist
snow	clouds	thunder
hail	tornado	sunshine
sleet	fog	cloudburst
wind	hurricane	lightning
blizzard	whirlwind	typhoon

II. Read and Answer

1. How does the wind help? How does it do harm?
2. How does rain help? How does it do harm?
3. Does thunder come before lightning or after? Why?
4. What is the difference between a hurricane and a tornado?
5. Have you ever seen a blizzard? A cloudburst? A hailstorm? A tornado? A hurricane? A whirlwind?

III. Write

1. Write five sentences. In each one, use a word from Part I.
2. Write a little story about the kind of weather you like best or least.

The Wolf and the Seven Kids

Brothers Grimm

Once upon a time a mother goat lived in a cozy little house with her seven little kids. Every day she went out to get food for them, and every day she told them to stay indoors because a great, ugly wolf was near who liked to eat little goats.

And every morning the little kids would say, "Yes, Mother, we will do what you say. Don't worry about us." One morning when the mother goat was in the woods getting

---

WORDS TO WATCH

fetch	stomach	dough	cottage	cupboard
gobbled	disorder	china	scissors	thread

tender leaves and green buds for her family, there came a knock at the door. "Open the door, children. Your mother is here with food."

But the voice was deep and gruff. The little kids knew it was not their mother, so they said, "You aren't our mother, and we won't open the door. You have a gruff voice, and we know you are the wolf."

So the wolf ran off to a shop and bought some honey, which he ate to make his voice soft and gentle. Then he came back and said, "Open the door, my dear children. It is your mother with something to eat."

But the wolf put his black paws on the window sill, so the kids said, "No, we won't open the door. You are not our mother. She doesn't have black feet. You are the wolf."

So the wolf ran off to a baker. "Put some dough and flour on my feet, Mr. Baker Man," he said. "I hurt both my front paws this morning." So the baker put some dough on the wolf's forepaws and sprinkled them with flour. Then back the wolf went to the cottage.

He rapped on the door. "Open the door, children," he said. "Here is your mother with something for all of you to eat, so open the door at once."

"Let us see your feet," said the little kids. The wolf put his white forepaws on the window sill. So the kids opened the door, and in ran the wolf.

The little kids were very frightened! They ran every which way trying to hide from the wolf. One ran under the kitchen

table, the second climbed into bed, the third got into the oven, the fourth under the kitchen sink, the fifth into the cupboard, the sixth under a chair. The seventh couldn't find any place to hide at first, but then he opened the little door of the big clock and hid inside, far back in a dark corner.

The wolf found them all but the youngest one, who was hidden in the clock. He gobbled them up and went out into a meadow. There he lay down under a tree and fell fast asleep.

When the mother goat came home, what a sight the house was! She found chairs and tables overturned, the bed in disorder, and china broken. She called for her children one after the other, but no one answered. Finally she called the youngest. A wee voice answered from the big clock, "Here I am, dear Mother." The goat took the kid out and heard how the wolf had come and eaten all the other children. The poor mother goat wept, but soon she and the little kid went outdoors and down into the meadow. There they saw the old wolf asleep, and as they watched him, they saw something move inside him.

"Are my children alive?" cried the mother goat. And quickly she ran back for a pair of scissors and a needle and thread. Quietly she cut open the wolf. Out popped one little kid, then the next, and the next, until all six were dancing around on the ground. The wolf had been so greedy that he had swallowed them whole. How happy they were! But there was no time to lose.

"Go and fetch some large stones," said the mother goat, "and we will put them in the wolf's stomach." So each little goat got a large stone, and the mother goat put the seven stones where the little kids had been and sewed them up. Then the goat and her children all ran away and hid.

Soon the wolf woke up, and he was very thirsty. He found a well and leaned over to drink, but the stones made him top-heavy, and in he tumbled. So the wicked wolf was drowned. The seven little kids and the mother danced joyfully around the well, and they lived happily ever after in their little cottage on the edge of the wood.

QUESTIONS

1. How did the wolf make the kids think he was their mother?
2. Do you think the kids disobeyed their mother when they opened the door and let the wolf in?
3. How did the mother goat save her children?
4. What did the mother goat do to the wolf?
5. What happened to the wolf?

AN AUTUMN RIDDLE

Anonymous

They are seen on the trees,
   They are seen on the ground.
They are seen in the air,
   Whirling softly around;

They sing rustling songs
   As our footsteps they hear,
And their name is well known,
   For they come every year.

Seeds and Civilization

Joan Elma Rahn

How long can we keep a ripe, juicy tomato or peach on the kitchen table? Usually for only a few days, because soon it becomes soft. Then it begins to rot and is no longer good to eat.

Fresh fruit will last longer in a refrigerator, but in a few weeks it too will begin to rot. If we wish to keep fruit still longer, we must freeze it, can it, or dry it.

How long can we keep dried beans or popping corn in the kitchen? We can keep them for many months or even a few years if the mice do not find them. As long as they do not become wet, beans and popping corn will remain good to eat. In the history of man, such seeds became very important as a source of food.

A long time ago—more than 10,000 years ago—there were no cities. There were no supermarkets in which to buy food. When fruit was ripe, people had to gather it and eat it within a few days. The same was true of vegetables. To get meat, people had to kill wild animals. Because meat could not be kept, it too had to be eaten within a few days.

All this meant that people had to go wherever fruits and vegetables were ripe, and they had to go where wild animals lived. They had to spend most of their time searching for food.

One of the foods people ate was the kernels of wild wheat plants. These kernels are fruits—not juicy fruits like peaches—but small, hard fruits. Each kernel contains one dry seed. The kernels can be stored for a long time, just like dried beans or popping corn.

Then one springtime someone dropped a few wheat kernels

on the ground. The kernels started growing. In a few days, the seeds inside the kernels sprouted into wheat plants. The plants grew, and in a few months they produced many new kernels. Someone else found that the wheat kernels could be stored over the winter and the seeds inside would sprout the following year.

People learned that if they planted seeds, they would later get much more food than if they searched for it in the forests and fields. So they planted beans, peas, and many other kinds of seeds. Each year they saved some of the seeds to plant the next year. Soon people learned to capture wild animals and feed them some of the kernels. They no longer had to hunt for fresh meat. For the first time, people had learned to be farmers.

Farmers must tend their plants. They must water them when the weather is dry, and must pull out weeds growing between the plants. Animals, too, must be cared for. People

built homes near the plants and animals. They spent less time traveling and more time thinking and getting new ideas.

Groups of farmers began to live together in villages. When people lived near each other, they would talk to each other and exchange food and tools.

Some people thought of better ways to take care of their plants. Others made new tools, like the plow, which helped them to raise more food. Still others became good at making clothes, or wagons, or weapons. Each person would make one or two kinds of things, and then exchange what he produced for things other people made.

Without seeds that could be stored and then planted, civilization might never have started. There might be no houses or clothing, but just enough food to keep people alive. Instead of reading this book, you might be in a forest or field looking for food. If you found it, all would be well for another day. If you did not, you would be hungry tonight.

Insects

I. Read and Spell

ant	bug	butterfly
bee	mosquito	moth
fly	caterpillar	termite
beetle	grasshopper	dragonfly
wasp	cricket	gnat
flea	ladybug	locust

II. Read and Answer

1. Which of these insects could bite or sting you?
2. Which of these insects live together in insect cities?
3. Which of these insects are harmful to people?
4. Which of these insects cannot fly?
5. Which of these insects make a loud noise?
6. Which of these insects help people?
7. Name some other insects.
8. What is an insect?

III. Write

1. Write five sentences. Let each one tell something about one of the insects in Part I.
2. Write a little story about an insect named in Part I.

The Bird, the Mouse, and the Bat

Anonymous

   Bird: What a strange mouse that is. It can fly.

Mouse: What a strange bird it is. It has fur.

   Bird: Oh, no! That is not a bird. We never show our ears.

Mouse: I am sure that it is not a mouse. Mice cannot fly.

   Bird: But look at its fur!

Mouse: But look at its wings!

   Bird: But look at its ears!

Mouse: I think it is more like a mouse than a bird; but who ever heard of a mouse that could fly?

   Bat: Are you talking about me?

   Bird: Yes, please tell us who you are.

Bat: My name is Bat. I heard you talking about me, but you called me a bird.

Bird: Oh, no! I called you a mouse.

Bat: What can a mouse do best?

Mouse: I can run.

Bat: But I cannot run at all.

Mouse: Then you are a poor kind of mouse.

Bat: I will tell you what I can do. I can fly as well as a bird.

Bird: But do you lay eggs in a nest?

Bat: No indeed! I have no nest and no eggs.

Bird: Then you are a poor kind of bird.

Mouse: Where do you sleep?

Bat: Oh, I hang by my toes in some old barn.

Bird: What a way to sleep!

Mouse: Who takes care of your little ones?

Bat: I carry them about with me until they are old enough to care for themselves.

Mouse: What a way to keep house!

Bird: Your wings are not like mine.

Bat: No, my wings are my hands too. I feel my way with them.

Bird: You fly as if you could not see very well.

Bat: That's true, but I can fly by listening to the echoes of my sounds. This means that even though I can't see, I can fly at night and in the darkest caves. That's something no bird or mouse can do!

Bird: That's true. But what are you eating?

Bat: I am catching flies now for my supper.

Mouse: Your eyes are small, and your ears are large. Can you hear better than you can see?

Bat: Yes, but I can touch better than I can see or hear. I would not give my wings for pretty ones like Bird's, nor would I give them for feet like those of Mouse.

Bird: I would not give up my nest to hang by my toes.

Mouse: Are your teeth as sharp as mine?

Bat: I have sharp teeth.

Mouse: I am afraid that you will bite.

Bat: I do bite when anyone tries to hurt me.

Mouse: Good-by, Bat. See how fast I can run!

Bird: Good-by, Bat. I am going home to my nest and my little ones.

Bat: Good-by. Please don't think that I would bite you. Why is everyone afraid of me? I do not wish to hurt anyone.

QUESTIONS

1. Why did the bird think the bat was like a mouse?
2. Why did the mouse think the bat was like a bird?
3. How is a bat different from a mouse? How is it different from a bird?
4. Have you ever seen a bat? Find out more about bats.

The Fox and the Crow

Aesop

One time a sly fox saw a crow fly from a kitchen window to the branch of a tree. The crow was holding a big piece of cheese in her beak.

"How I would like to have that piece of cheese," said the fox to himself. The fox thought and thought about how he could get the cheese. Then he went over to the foot of the tree and said, "Good morning, Mistress Crow. How pretty you look today. You are the most beautiful of all birds. And no bird in the world can sing more sweetly than you. How I would love to hear you sing!"

WORDS TO WATCH

beautiful   stretched   flatterer

72

The crow was very pleased to hear all these nice things said about her.

"I will be glad to sing you a little song," she said. She stretched out her neck, opened her beak wide, and sang at the top of her lungs, "Caw, caw, caw!"

At once the big piece of cheese fell to the ground, and the hungry fox gobbled it up.

"Thank you," said the fox. "That was very good cheese."

"Oh, what have I done!" said the crow to herself. "I will never trust a flatterer again."

QUESTIONS

1. Do you think the fox was clever? Why?
2. Do you think that the crow sang as sweetly as the fox said she could?
3. What did the crow learn from the fox?

hot and Cold from One Mouth

Aesop

Once there lived a woman who cut wood in the forest. When winter came, her hands got very cold. She put down her ax and breathed into her hands to warm them. A dwarf who lived in the forest saw this and asked her, "Why do you do this?"

"My hands are cold, and I want to warm them with my breath," explained the woodcutter. This answer satisfied the dwarf.

Later in the day the woodcutter built a fire to warm her food. The dwarf was still watching her curiously. The woodcutter was very hungry. She did not want to wait until her food had cooled, and she ate right out of the pot. But as the soup was still rather hot, she blew on every spoonful she ate. That amazed the dwarf very much, and he asked, "Why do you blow on the spoon just as you breathed on your cold hands?"

The woodcutter answered, "I want to cool off my hot soup."

This was too much for the dwarf to understand. He said, "You are a strange creature. From your mouth you sometimes breathe warm, sometimes cold. I don't want to stay with you any longer." And he ran away as fast as his legs could carry him.

QUESTIONS

1. What was the woodcutter trying to do when she breathed on her hands?
2. What was she trying to do when she was blowing on her soup?
3. How can she breathe both warm and cold from her mouth?

Who Loves the Trees Best?

Alice May Douglas

Who loves the trees best? "I," said the Spring.
"Their leaves so beautiful to them I bring."

Who loves the trees best? "I," Summer said.
"I give them blossoms, white, yellow, red."

Who loves the trees best? "I," said the Fall.
"I give luscious fruits, bright tints to all."

Who loves the trees best? "I love them best,"
Harsh Winter answered. "I give them rest."

Trees

I. Read and Spell

pine	cherry	aspen
elm	maple	cedar
apple	fir	birch
oak	magnolia	walnut
palm	redwood	poplar
ash	spruce	beech
weeping willow	hickory	dogwood

II. Read and Answer

1. Which of the trees in Part I have leaves that look like needles?
2. Have you eaten the fruit of any trees? Which?
3. Which tree in Part I grows the tallest?
4. How are trees useful to human beings?

III. Write

1. Write five sentences. Use a word from Part I in each sentence.
2. Write a little story about why you like trees.

The Three Wishes

Swedish Fairy Tale

There was once a very poor man who lived with his wife in a humble little cottage. Every day he went into the forest to chop wood. One day when he was in the forest, he said to himself, "Oh, dear, I am so unhappy! I am poor, and I have to work so hard all day long. My wife is hungry, and I am hungry too. Oh, I am very unhappy indeed!"

At that moment a beautiful fairy appeared before him. She

WORDS TO WATCH			
humble	disappeared	fortunate	granted
promise	empire	diamonds	prefer
insisted	sensible	patience	sausage

said to him, "My poor man, I heard everything that you just said. I am very sorry for you and would like to help you. Ask whatever you like, and your first three wishes shall be granted."

Then just as suddenly as she had come, the fairy disappeared.

The poor man felt very happy now, and he said, "I shall go home, and I shall tell my wife how the fairy has granted me three wishes."

He ran back to his cottage and called to his wife: "Wife, Wife, I am very fortunate. I saw a fairy in the forest, and she said I could have three wishes. 'Ask for anything you like,' the fairy said, 'and your wish shall be granted!' Oh, Wife, I am so happy."

"I am happy too," said the woman. "Come, let us go into the house, my dear, and let us decide what our wishes shall be."

The man went into the little cottage and sat down at the table. "I am hungry, Wife," he said. "I would like some dinner. While we eat, we can talk about the fairy and the three wishes."

The poor man and his wife sat down at the table and started to eat their dinner and to talk about the good fairy's promise.

"We can ask for great riches if we want to," said the man.

"Yes," the wife agreed, "we can ask for a beautiful house."

"We can even ask for a whole empire if we want to," said the man.

And his wife replied, "Yes, we can ask for pearls and diamonds by the hundred."

"We can ask for a big family," the man added, "five boys and five girls."

"Oh, I would prefer six boys and four girls," insisted the wife.

The man and the woman went on talking like that, but they couldn't decide what three wishes would be the most sensible of all.

The man ate his soup in silence and looked at the dry bread on his plate. "Oh, I wish I had a great big sausage for dinner!" he said.

At that very instant a great big sausage fell onto the table. Naturally the man was very surprised to see the sausage, and so was his wife.

"Oh, Husband," the wife said, "you have been very foolish. You asked for a silly old sausage, and so one of the wishes has been granted. Now there are only two wishes left."

"Yes," said the man, "I have been very foolish. But we still have two wishes. We can ask for great riches and an empire."

"Yes," his wife agreed, "we can still ask for riches and an empire, but we can't ask for ten children. And it's your fault for demanding a sausage. You would rather have a sausage than a big family."

The poor woman went on talking like that, complaining and saying over and over again, "It's all your fault for being so foolish!"

Finally the man lost his patience and said, "I am tired of your complaining! I wish that the sausage were hanging from the end of your nose!"

The next second the sausage was hanging from the end of his wife's nose. Naturally the poor woman was greatly surprised, and so was her husband.

The woman started to complain again, more loudly than before. "Oh, my husband," she said, "you have been very, very foolish. First you asked for a sausage, and then you wished that the sausage were hanging from the end of my nose. That makes two wishes. Two foolish wishes! Now we have only one more wish!"

"Yes," the man agreed, "but we can still ask for great riches."

"What good are riches," the woman complained, "if I have a sausage hanging from the end of my nose? Why, I look ridiculous! And it's all your fault!"

The poor woman started to cry, and the poor man said, "Oh, I wish that sausage weren't here at all!"

Instantly the sausage disappeared, and the man and the woman were right back where they started, as poor as ever. They both complained, but it didn't do them any good, for they had used up their wishes.

The three wishes had been granted, and still they had no riches, no empire, no pearls and diamonds, no little boys and no little girls.

And they didn't even have any sausage for dinner!

QUESTIONS

1. What did the poor man and the poor woman want with their three wishes?
2. How did they use up each of their wishes?
3. Why didn't the poor man and poor woman use their wishes for what they really wanted?
4. If you had been the poor man, how would you have used the third wish?
5. Write a story telling what you would wish for if you could make three wishes.

THE COW

Robert Louis Stevenson

The friendly cow all red and white,
   I love with all my heart:
She gives me cream, with all her might,
   To eat with apple-tart.

She wanders lowing here and there,
   And yet she cannot stray,
All in the pleasant open air,
   The pleasant light of day;

And blown by all the winds that pass
   And wet with all the showers,
She walks among the meadow grass
   And eats the meadow flowers.

The Sweet Pudding

Brothers Grimm

Once upon a time a little girl lived all alone with her mother. She was a very good girl, but they were so poor that they had nothing left to eat. The girl gathered berries and roots in the forest.

One day she met an old woman, who seemed to know how poor they were. She gave the girl a little pot and said, "If you want good sweet pudding just say to the pot, 'Little pot, boil!' It will cook the best pudding you have ever tasted. Then after you have had enough to eat, say, 'Little pot, stop!' The pot will stop cooking right away." The girl thanked the old woman and couldn't wait to try it out.

The girl ran home and showed her mother the magic pot. Now they were no longer poor nor hungry. They ate all the sweet pudding they could, day after day.

Once when the girl had gone for a walk, the mother said, "Little pot, boil!" It cooked pudding until she could not eat another bite. But the mother did not know how to stop the little pot from cooking pudding. So it cooked on and on, and on and on. The pudding came out of the pot and into the kitchen, into all the other rooms, out on the street, and into the next house.

Soon the street was filled with sweet pudding, and it ran into one house after another. It seemed as though the little

pot wanted to cook for the whole world. Nobody knew what to do, and it was a terrible mess.

Finally, when almost all the houses were filled with pudding, the child came home and said, "Little pot, stop!" Immediately the little pot stopped cooking. Anyone who wanted to go back into town, first had to eat his way through the sweet pudding.

QUESTIONS

1. What kind of pot did the old woman give the little girl?
2. What did she have to say to it to make pudding? To stop it from making pudding?
3. What happened when the mother did not know how to stop the little pot?

Thanksgiving Day

Lydia Marie Child

Over the river and through the wood,
  To Grandfather's house we go;
    The horse knows the way
    To carry the sleigh
  Through the white and drifted snow.

Over the river and through the wood—
  Oh, how the wind does blow!
    It stings the toes
    And bites the nose
  As over the ground we go.

Over the river and through the wood,
  To have a first-rate play.
    Hear the bells ring,
    "Ting-a-ling-ding!"
  Hurrah for Thanksgiving Day!

Over the river and through the wood,
  Trot fast, my dapple-gray!
    Spring over the ground
    Like a hunting hound,
  For this is Thanksgiving Day.

Over the river and through the wood,
  And straight through the barnyard gate. . .
    We seem to go
    Extremely slow—
  It is so hard to wait!

Over the river and through the wood—
  Now Grandmother's cap I spy!
    Hurrah for the fun!
    Is the pudding done?
  Hurrah for the pumpkin pie!

Fruits and Vegetables

I. Read and Spell

plum	banana	apricot
beets	pear	lemon
orange	potato	corn
spinach	squash	peas
lime	grapefruit	carrots
apple	peach	beans

II. Read and Answer

1. Which of the words in Part I are names of fruits?
2. Which are vegetables?
3. Name four kinds of berries.
4. Name some more fruits and vegetables.
5. Which vegetables grow under the ground?
6. What kind of fruit do you like most?
7. What kind of vegetable do you like least?

III. Write

Write five sentences. Let each one tell something about a fruit or vegetable.

The Ox Who Won the Forfeit

Indian Tale

Long ago a man owned a very strong ox. The owner was so proud of his ox that he boasted to every man he met about how strong his ox was.

One day the owner went into a village. He said to the men there, "I will pay a forfeit of a thousand pieces of silver if my strong ox cannot draw a line of one hundred wagons."

The men laughed and said, "Very well, bring your ox, and we will tie a hundred wagons in a line and see your ox draw them along."

WORDS TO WATCH			
owner	boasted	forfeit	hundred
yoked	wretch	rascal	garland

So the man brought his ox into the village. A crowd gathered to see the sight. The hundred carts were in line, and the strong ox was yoked to the first wagon.

Then the owner whipped his ox and said, "Get up, you wretch! Get along, you rascal!"

But the ox had never been talked to in that way, and he stood still. Neither the blows nor the hard names could make him move.

At last the poor man paid his forfeit and went sadly home. There he threw himself on his bed and cried, "Why did that strong ox act so? Many a time he has moved heavier loads easily. Why did he shame me before all those people?"

At last he got up and went about his work. When he went to feed the ox that night, the ox turned to him and said, "Why did you call me 'wretch' and 'rascal'? You never called me hard names before."

Then the man said, "I will never treat you badly again. I am sorry I whipped you and called you names. I will never do so any more. Forgive me."

"Very well," said the ox. "Tomorrow I will go into the village and draw the one hundred carts for you. You have always been a kind master until today. Tomorrow you shall gain what you have lost."

The next morning the owner fed the ox well and hung a garland of flowers about his neck. When they went into the village, the men laughed at the man again.

They said, "Did you come back to lose more money?"

"Today I will pay a forfeit of two thousand pieces of silver if my ox is not strong enough to pull the one hundred carts," said the owner.

So again the carts were placed in a line, and the ox was yoked to the first. A crowd came to watch again. The owner said, "Good ox, show how strong you are! You fine, fine creature!" And he patted his neck and stroked his sides.

At once the ox pulled with all his strength. The carts moved on until the last cart stood where the first had been.

Then the crowd shouted, and they paid back the forfeit the man had lost saying, "Your ox is the strongest ox we have ever seen."

And the ox and the man went home happy.

QUESTIONS

1. Why did the ox not pull the wagons the first time?
2. Why did the ox pull them the second time?
3. What can you learn from this story?

The Busy Workers

Anonymous

Squirrel: Good morning, Cousin Beaver. What are you doing?

Beaver: I am making a dam. We must have a home where we can keep warm. It will be cold before long.

Squirrel: It is a pity that your tail is so flat and hard. See how thick and warm mine is! I can wrap it around me. When I am in my hole in the tree, I do not feel the cold at all.

Beaver: I thought you lived in the tops of the trees.

Squirrel: So I do in good weather. We stay there in the summer. In the fall we come down into our warm nests in the tree to spend the winter. All our nuts are there.

Beaver: We keep our nuts and twigs in our winter house, too. It is much safer than to leave them on the trees.

Squirrel: Why do you take so much trouble to build a dam? That hole in the bank must make a good house just as it is.

Beaver: Yes, but we like the water. And we like to build a high dam near our house, because if there is deep water around us, the wolves and other animals will leave us alone. Also, in wintertime the deep water cannot freeze to the bottom.

Squirrel: How will you make a dam?

Beaver: We will cut some trees, up there by the bridge, and float them down the stream.

Squirrel: Why do you not use these trees?

Beaver: We will use a few large ones if we can make them fall in the right place.

Squirrel: Won't the water run through your dam?

Beaver: No. We plaster it well with mud and grass.

Squirrel: Do you cut those big trees with your teeth?

Beaver: Yes. That is what our sharp teeth are for. We can cut large trees in that way.

Squirrel: I should think your teeth would wear off if you cut very large trees.

Beaver: They do wear off, but they soon grow long again. I see you have sharp teeth too.

Squirrel: Yes. That is so we can cut through the hard shell of a nut. I must go now. I have to get nuts enough for winter. Good-by.

Beaver: Good-by. I must go back to work, too.

1. How is a beaver like a squirrel?
2. How is he different from a squirrel?
3. How does a beaver make a dam?
4. Find out more about beavers.

The Raccoon's Tail

American Folk Rhyme

The raccoon's tail is ring-around,
The possum's tail is bare;
The rabbit has no tail at all,
Only a big bunch of hair.

Animals

I. Read and Spell

dog	seal	sheep	elephant
cow	camel	lion	gorilla
horse	donkey	bear	hippopotamus
cat	pig	monkey	leopard
deer	wolf	goat	chimpanzee
tiger	zebra	walrus	rhinoceros
fox	rabbit	giraffe	kangaroo

II. Read and Answer

1. Which of these animals would you find in a house or on a farm?
2. Which of these animals do not live in America?
3. What are the babies of these animals called?

    sheep   goats   bears   cats   dogs   cows

4. What is the name of the meat that comes from these animals?

    cows   sheep   pigs

5. Which animal do you think is the most valuable to people?

III. Write

1. Write five sentences. In each one, use a word from Part I.
2. Write a story about an animal in Part I.

I. A. You have read these stories in Part Two of your book. Tell what each one is about.

A Parakeet Named Dreidel

The Tale of the Clever Deer

The Wolf and the Seven Kids

Seeds and Civilization

The Bird, the Mouse, and the Bat

The Fox and the Crow

Hot and Cold from One Mouth

The Three Wishes

The Sweet Pudding

The Ox Who Won the Forfeit

The Busy Workers

B. Which of these stories did you like best? Why?

II. A. Memorize a poem you read in Part Two and recite it to the class.

B. Copy the poem you like best in Part Two of your book. Copy it carefully.

Part Three
Fables and Folk Tales

We've read of birds and bugs
And lots of other things,
And now we're going to read
Of cabbages and kings.

The Boy and the Worm

Anonymous

One time a little boy was playing in his backyard. In the grass he saw a worm. He watched the worm for a long time. Then he said, "What an ugly thing you are! You have no hair, no legs, and I don't think you even have eyes."

"That doesn't matter," said the worm. "All worms are like that. We get along fine."

"But do you know how to do anything?" asked the boy. "The animals run about and the birds fly and sing. You cannot do any of these things."

"True," said the worm. "I cannot do those things."

"I know how to do everything," said the boy. "I even know how to read and write."

"I do not need to know how to read and write," said the worm. "But, tell me, do you know how to live in the world all by yourself? Can you feed yourself and take care of yourself without the help of your parents?"

"No, but I am still very young," said the boy.

"But I am much younger than you, and yet I can feed myself and take care of myself without any help. And besides, did you ever see a worm that could talk?"

QUESTIONS

1. What did the boy say to the worm?
2. What did the worm say to the boy?
3. Who is smarter, the boy or the worm? Why?

Kind Hearts Are Gardens

Anonymous

Kind hearts are gardens,
Kind thoughts are roots,
Kind words are blossoms,
Kind deeds are fruits.

The Bremen Town Musicians

Brothers Grimm

Once upon a time there lived an old donkey who had carried many a heavy sack of grain to the mill for his master. Now he was worn out and weary and could work no more. His master wanted to get him out of the way, but the donkey said to himself, "An ill wind is blowing! I had better get out of here while I can still use my four legs." And he started out for the town of Bremen, thinking that he might become a town musician to make a living.

He had not gone very far, when he came upon a big hunting dog who panted like one too tired to go one step further. "Now, now, old hound," said the donkey, "why are you panting so hard?"

"Ach," said the dog sadly, "I am old and getting weaker every day. I am not fit any more to go hunting with my master, and that's why he wanted to kill me. But I took to my heels and here I am. A lot of good it does me now, not knowing how to earn my food!"

"I have an idea, good friend," said the donkey. "I am on my way to Bremen, and there I plan to become a town musician. Come along with me and take up music too! I'll play the lute and you can pound the drum." The dog was content with this plan and the two traveled on together.

Before long they met a cat whose face looked as sad and long as a three day rain. "Well, old Whisker-wiper, what has crossed your path today?" asked the donkey.

"Who can be cheerful when his life is at stake?" answered the cat. "I am getting on in years, my teeth are no longer sharp, and I find it easier to sit by the fire and dream than to run after mice. That's why my mistress wanted to drown me. I ran away and here I am, but what shall I do now?"

"Come along with us," said the donkey, "we are going to Bremen to be musicians. You surely have talent for singing at night, so you can become a town musician like us." The cat liked the idea and joined them.

Soon the three runaways came to a farmyard, and there on top of the gate sat a rooster, crowing away at the top of his lungs. "You crow loud enough to pierce our bones and marrow," said the donkey. "What's up?"

"My mistress told the cook to put me in the soup for Sunday dinner tomorrow. She will not have any pity on me, and my head will be cut off tonight. So now I am crowing at the top of my voice as long as I am still able."

"Now, now, Redhead," said the donkey, "you'll find something better than death anywhere! Why don't you travel with us to Bremen and be a musician? You have a fine lusty voice and when the four of us are making music together, it will be something to listen to!" The rooster agreed, and so all four of them traveled on together.

The town of Bremen, however, was far away and they could not reach it in one day. Towards evening they came to a forest where they decided to spend the night. The donkey and the dog lay down under a big tree, the cat climbed to the lower branches, and the rooster flew up to the very top. Just before he closed his eyes however, the rooster once more took a long look in all four directions. All of a sudden he saw a tiny light glowing among the trees. "I can see a light," he shouted down to his companions. "There has to be a house not far away!"

"We must get up and go there," said the donkey. "These quarters here are none too comfortable."

"I would not mind a few bones with a little meat," said the dog. So they started out toward the light, which became bigger and bigger, until at last they found themselves in front of a brightly lit house of robbers. The donkey, being the tallest, crept to the window and looked in. "What do you see, Long-ears?" asked the rooster.

"I see a table covered with delicious food and drink and robbers sitting around it and having a good time," answered the donkey.

"That would be just the thing for us!" said the rooster.

"Oh my, yes, if only we could be sitting in there," replied the donkey.

The animals put their heads together and tried to think of a way to chase the robbers away. At last they settled upon a plan. The donkey had to stand at the window with his forefeet on the ledge. The dog jumped on the donkey's back, the cat climbed on the dog's back, and finally the rooster flew up and perched himself on top of the cat. This done, the donkey gave

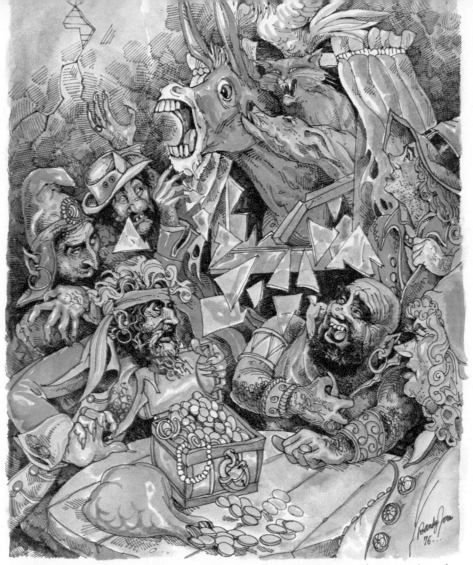

a signal and they all started to make their music—as loud as they possibly could. The donkey brayed, the dog barked, the cat meowed, and the rooster crowed! Then they burst through the window right into the middle of the room, the glass crashing and clattering all around them. The robbers, sure that the devil himself had broken into their house, jumped up and fled, terror-stricken, far into the forest. The four musicians, however, sat down at the table, well content with what was left and ate as though they had to eat enough

for four weeks. Then they blew out the light and looked for a
place to sleep—each according to his nature and his own idea
of comfort. The donkey went outside and lay down on top of
the manure pile. The dog stretched out behind the back door.
The cat curled up on the hearth next to the warm ashes, and
the rooster perched himself on top of the roof. And as they
were very tired after their long day's journey, they soon were
fast asleep.

Some time after midnight, when the robbers could not see
any more lights burning in their house, they came out from
their hiding place in the woods. Everything seemed quiet and
safe and the robber chief said, "We should not have let
ourselves get frightened so easily." He ordered one of the
robbers to go to the house and look around. The robber did
as he was told and, finding everything peaceful and quiet, he
went to the kitchen to light a lamp. Mistaking the glowing,
fiery eyes of the cat for live coals, he held out his match to
kindle it. But the cat did not think this a joke and sprang right

into his face, spitting and scratching. The robber, frightened
out of his wits, started to run out of the back door, but the
dog, who lay there, leaped up and bit him in the leg. And
when the robber ran past the manure pile, the donkey gave
him a hearty kick with his hind hoof. But the rooster, who
had been awakened by all this noise and thought it was
morning, lustily crowed, "Keekerikee! Keekerikee!" The
terrified robber ran as though his life depended on it and did
not stop until he reached his chief.

"What horrors!" he gasped. "In the house by the fire sits a
dreadful witch. She hissed at me and scratched my face with
her long fingernails. In front of the door stands a man with a
knife, and he stabbed my leg as I ran out. In the yard lurks a
black monster which beat me with a wooden club, and up on
the roof sits the judge and he screamed, 'Keep the thief here!
Keep the thief here!' That was too much for me and I took to
my heels."

From then on none of the robbers ever dared to go back to
the house or even come near it. Our four town musicians,
however, liked their new home so well that they lived in it
happy and contented for the rest of their lives.

An Emerald Is as Green as Grass

Christina Rossetti

An emerald is as green as grass;
  A ruby red as blood;
A sapphire shines as blue as heaven;
  A flint lies in the mud.

A diamond is a brilliant stone;
  To catch the world's desire;
An opal holds a fiery spark;
  But a flint holds fire.

WORDS TO WATCH			
emerald	ruby	sapphire	flint
heaven	brilliant	fiery	opal

Antonyms

I. Read and Spell

up	down	heavy	light
over	under	poor	rich
in	out	true	false
off	on	hard	soft
light	dark	odd	even
good	bad	new	old
back	front	large	small
left	right	tall	short

II. Read and Answer

1. What are the antonyms of these words?

floor	raw	rough	open
now	beginning	go	fat
more	tight	all	high

2. Think of three more pairs of opposite words.

III. Write

Write five sentences. In each one, use a pair of words from Part I.

Christmas Is Coming

Marianne Carus

"Only two more weeks till Christmas," says Mother.

"Hurray, hurray!" the children shout with joy.

Mother puts flour and dough on the table, and Joan kneads it and rolls it out. It is hard work, because dough has to be very thin. Jimmy and Edward help cut out cookies, and Mother puts them on the cookie sheet. They are lined up like soldiers: Christmas trees, angels, bells, stars, snowmen, and lots of other shapes. Now the cookies are baking, and the whole house smells like Christmas—cinnamon, ginger, honey—mmm!!

WORDS TO WATCH		
dough	cinnamon	Jingle Bells
cookie sheet	ginger	reindeer

There are secrets everywhere. When Mother comes into the room, Joan quickly hides something under the table.

"Please don't look, Mother," she calls. She is working on a surprise for Christmas. All of a sudden when Father and Mother talk together, they start whispering. If the children could only hear what they are whispering about! Secrets, secrets, and nobody should find out about secrets before Christmas.

Snow is falling softly and silently. Streets and roofs and fences and cars are covered with white blankets. The children have to put food out for the birds.

In the evenings they sit in front of the cozy fire and sing Christmas carols: "Joy to the World," "Jingle Bells," "Away in a Manger." The children talk about Santa Claus coming through the snow with his sled and his reindeer.

"You have to be good to each other," Mother says. "Santa Claus comes only to good children."

Joan and Jimmy are writing their lists for Santa. They know what they want. Edward cannot make up his mind. He wants to talk to Santa when he comes to school. After Santa has come, there will be no more school until the New Year has come.

In Sunday school they will have a Christmas party, and Joan will be an angel in the Christmas play. She will wear a long white gown and a silver crown and look like a Fairy Queen. It is exciting just to think about it!

The children will all help decorate the tree and keep the house in order. They will hang up their stockings, put out cookies for Santa Claus, and then . . . Christmas morning!

"Still two more weeks till Christmas, Mother?" asks little Edward. "But why can't time go a little bit faster just before Christmas?

QUESTIONS

1. How are the children helping before Christmas?
2. Who has secrets and why?
3. What is the family doing in the evening?
4. What is going on in school before Christmas?

OTTO

Gwendolyn Brooks

It's Christmas Day. I did not get
The presents that I hoped for. Yet,
It is not nice to frown or fret.

To frown or fret would not be fair.
My Dad must never know I care
It's hard enough for him to bear.

111

Why the Bear Has a Short Tail

American Folk Tale

One cold morning when the fox was coming up the road with some fish, he met the bear.

"Good morning, Mr. Fox," said the bear.

"Good morning, Mr. Bear," said the fox. "The morning is brighter because I have met you."

"Those are very good fish, Mr. Fox," said the bear. "I have not eaten such fish for many a day. Where do you find them?"

"I have been fishing, Mr. Bear," answered the fox.

"If I could catch such fish as those, I should like to go fishing. But I do not know how to fish."

"It would be very easy for you to learn, Mr. Bear," said the fox. "You are so big and strong that you can do anything."

"Will you teach me, Mr. Fox?" asked the bear.

"I would not tell everybody, but you are such a good friend that I will teach you. Come to this pond, and I will show you how to fish through the ice."

So the fox and the bear went to the frozen pond, and the fox showed the bear how to make a hole in the ice.

"That is easy for you," said the fox, "but many an animal could not have made that hole. Now comes the secret. You must put your tail down into the water and keep it there. That is not easy, and not every animal could do it, for the water is very cold. But you are a learned animal, Mr. Bear. You know that the secret of catching fish is to keep your tail in the water a long time. Then when you pull it up, you will pull with it as many fish as I have."

The bear put his tail down into the water, and the fox went away. The sun rose high in the heavens. Still the bear sat with his tail through the hole in the ice, for he thought, "When an animal is really learned, he will not fear a little cold."

It began to get dark, and the bear said, "Now I will pull the fish out of the water. How good they will be!" He pulled and pulled, but not a fish came out. Worse than that, when he finally broke himself loose, not all of his tail came out, for the end of it was frozen to the ice.

He went slowly down the road, growling angrily, "I wish I could find that fox." But the cunning fox was curled up in his warm nest, and whenever he thought of the bear, he laughed.

Tracks in the Snow

Marchette Chute

This was a mouse who played around
All by himself one night,
Dancing under the winter moon
Forward and left and right.

This was a pheasant walking by,
Out with a friend or two—
This was a rabbit running fast,
The way rabbits do.

This was a squirrel who found a nut—
This was a chickadee—
And this uncommon sort of track
I think was probably me.

The Garden Year

Sarah Coleridge

January brings the snow,
Makes our feet and fingers glow.

February brings the rain,
Thaws the frozen lake again.

March brings breezes, loud and shrill,
To stir the dancing daffodil.

April brings the primrose sweet,
Scatters daisies at our feet.

May brings flocks of pretty lambs
Skipping by their fleecy dams.

June brings tulips, lilies, roses,
Fills the children's hands with posies.

WORDS TO WATCH			
shrill	daffodil	primrose	fleecy
posies	gillyflowers	sheaves	borne
pheasant	sleet	blazing	treat

Hot July brings cooling showers,
Apricots, and gillyflowers.

August brings the sheaves of corn;
Then the harvest home is borne.

Warm September brings the fruit;
Sportsmen then begin to shoot.

Fresh October brings the pheasant;
Then to gather nuts is pleasant.

Dull November brings the blast;
Then the leaves are whirling fast.

Chill December brings the sleet,
Blazing fire, and Christmas treat.

QUESTIONS

1. Which month do you like best? Why?
2. Write a paragraph about the month you like best.

The Months of the Year

I. Read and Spell

January	May	September
February	June	October
March	July	November
April	August	December

II. Read and Answer

1. Which month do you think is the hardest to spell?
2. What is the shortest month of the year? What are the longest months?
3. How many months are in a year?
4. How many weeks are in a month?
5. What months are in these seasons of the year?

     spring   summer   fall   winter

III. Read, Write, and Memorize

Thirty days hath September,
April, June, and November;
All the rest have thirty-one,
Except February alone,
Which has four and twenty-four
Till leap year gives it one day more.

Androcles and the Lion
Classical Tale

Androcles was a brave soldier and one of the emperor's favorites. But once he displeased the emperor by shooting a deer that the emperor had missed. So the man was sold to be a slave and sent far from his home.

After he had been a slave for several years, he escaped. He wandered off into the hills and deserts trying to find his way back to his own land. One very hot day he crawled into a cave to get out of the sun. He was very hungry, but he hoped to find something to eat later in the day. While he was resting from his wanderings, he heard a strange sound. He knew that an animal was coming into the cave. But he could not tell what it was. The steps did not sound like the steps of any animal that he knew. But he was frightened, and he held his breath so as to make no sound.

As he waited, holding his breath, the animal came nearer. It was a lion. But he did not look fierce. He did not walk as if he were the King of Beasts. In fact, he was limping on three legs and holding one of his front paws in the air.

WORDS TO WATCH

Androcles	favorite	displeased	arena
emperor	recognized	desert	squeak
tongue	protected		prisoner

118

Androcles felt so sorry for the lion that he forgot to be afraid. The lion walked up to him and stopped right in front of him. He held up his paw and made a soft m-i-a-o-w, like a sad and hungry kitten, only louder. Then Androcles saw that the poor lion had a thorn in his paw.

Androcles bent over and gently pulled the thorn out of the lion's foot. The lion squeaked a little when the thorn came out. But then the lion saw that he could walk on all four feet again. He purred and shook his head gently at Androcles. Then he turned around and walked out of the cave.

Androcles wandered about for days and weeks. He lived as best he could on roots and berries and nuts. At last he came to a camp made up of many tents. He was very glad, because he thought that now he could get food and be safe from wild animals. But when he came to the camp, he saw that it was filled with the emperor's soldiers. The captain recognized Androcles. They made a prisoner of him and after a while brought him back to Rome.

The emperor disliked Androcles even more now, because he had run away from his master. So the emperor decided on a very cruel punishment. He ordered Androcles put into the arena, where a hungry lion would eat him. There Androcles stood, and the gate to the lion's cage was opened.

The lion came out growling and sniffing. He walked about as if he were looking for something to eat. Soon he came to where Androcles was standing and waiting, expecting to be attacked the very next minute. But when the lion looked at

Androcles, instead of springing on him, he began to lick his hand gently with his tongue. It was the same lion that Androcles had helped that day in the cave!

Everybody was amazed. Word was brought to the emperor that Androcles must be a strange magician, for the lion would not eat him. The emperor ordered Androcles brought before him and asked him to explain what his power was that protected him from the lion.

Then Androcles told the story of the lion in the desert and how he had removed the thorn from the lion's paw. When the emperor heard this story, he saw what a brave and good man Androcles was. The emperor forgave him and took him back into his favor.

QUESTIONS

1. Why was Androcles sold as a slave?
2. Why was the lion limping?
3. What did Androcles do that showed he was brave?
4. Why was Androcles sent back to Rome as a prisoner?
5. How did the emperor plan to punish Androcles?
6. Why did the people think Androcles was a magician?
7. Why did the emperor take Androcles back into his favor?

THE MILKMAID
AND HER PAIL

Aesop

One time a milkmaid was on her way to market with a pail of milk on her head.

As she was walking along, she said to herself, "With the money I get from this milk, I am going to buy some setting eggs. From the eggs I will get some chicks. Then I will raise the chicks until they are big enough to sell. With the money I get from the chickens, I will buy a beautiful gown. When I wear the gown, I will look so beautiful that everyone will admire me. But I shall act very proudly. I will shrug my shoulders like this."

WORDS TO WATCH

market	admire	raise
money	proudly	shrugged

122

And as she shrugged her shoulders, she tossed her head back. The pail of milk tumbled down, and the milk spilled all over the ground.

"Oh dear!" exclaimed the milkmaid. "Now there will be no gown, and no one will admire me. I won't even have any chickens or any eggs, and now I don't even have the milk. But I have learned one thing: Don't count your chickens before they are hatched."

1. Why did the milk spill all over the ground?
2. Why was the milkmaid foolish?
3. What do you think is meant when someone says, "Don't count your chickens before they are hatched"?

How Creatures Move

Anonymous

The lion walks on padded paws,
The squirrel leaps from limb to limb,
While flies can crawl straight up a wall,
And seals can dive and swim.
The worm, he wiggles all around,
The monkey swings by his tail,
And birds may hop upon the ground,
Or spread their wings and sail.
But boys and girls have much more fun;
They leap and dance
And walk and run.

THE QUARREL

Old Fable

One time the parts of the human body began to quarrel. They became very angry and decided that they would not help one another any more.

"We are not going to walk any more," said the legs to the other parts of the body. "You will have to get around as best you can," they said.

"We are not going to work for you any more," said the hands. "From now on, work for yourselves."

WORDS TO WATCH

quarrel	decided	healthy
human	members	friends

"Why should I feed you any more?" said the mouth, "After this, you can feed yourselves."

"What do we care for you?" said the eyes. "We are not going to see for you any longer."

And so the parts of the body would not help one another. The legs would not walk, the hands would not work, the mouth would not eat, and the eyes would not see.

Soon all the members of the body became weaker and weaker, and the body also became weak and thin.

Then the members of the body saw that they must not quarrel any longer. They decided to be friends again. The legs began to walk again, the hands went back to work, the mouth ate again, and the eyes began to see again. Soon the members became as strong as before, and the body became very healthy.

QUESTIONS

---

1. What happened to the body when the legs, the hands, the mouth, and the eyes would not help each other?
2. What can you learn from this story?

Parts of the Body

I. Read and Spell

ear	brain	elbow	mouth
nose	arm	wrist	ankle
face	cheek	hand	forehead
lips	chin	finger	skin
head	neck	throat	hair
eye	shoulder	heel	thumb
heart	stomach	leg	blood
lungs	tongue	knee	muscles
foot	toe	back	nerves

II. Read and Answer

1. Why are the heart, the lungs, the brain, and the stomach important to us?
2. The five senses are sight, hearing, taste, smell, and touch. What part of the body do we use for each of the senses?
3. Which of the five senses do you think is most important?

III. Write

Write a little story about what one part of your body does.

Sleeping Beauty

Brothers Grimm

Once upon a time there lived a king and a queen who wanted a child more than anything in the world. After many years when a little girl was born, they were overjoyed. The princess was so lovely that the proud king ordered a splendid feast.

Of the thirteen fairies living in his kingdom, he invited only twelve, as he had only twelve golden dinner plates. When the feast was almost over, each of the twelve fairies offered a special gift to the little princess.

WORDS TO WATCH			
revenge	courtiers	parted	curse
spindle	sizzling	doves	kingdom
confusion	flax	pluck	grieve

"You shall be the fairest of all," said one fairy.

"And the happiest," said another.

"You shall be loved by everyone for your good heart and your kindness," said the third.

"Nobody will have more riches than you," said the next.

"You shall sing like a nightingale," said another.

When eleven of the fairies had given their gifts, the princess had everything that one could wish for. As the twelfth and last fairy was just about to speak, suddenly the door to the big hall opened. In came the thirteenth fairy, who wanted to get her revenge for not being invited. She bent over the sleeping child and hissed, "When the princess is fifteen years old, she shall prick her finger with a spindle and die."

Without saying another word, the angry fairy turned and left. Everyone was terrified, and there was great confusion. But then the twelfth fairy, who had not yet spoken, stepped forward quickly. "Do not grieve," she said to the king and queen. "I cannot undo the bad fairy's curse, but I can change it. The princess shall not die, but shall fall asleep for one hundred years after she pricks her finger with the spindle."

The next morning the king ordered all spindles in the country burned at once.

As the years went by, all wishes of the good fairies came true. The princess was so beautiful, kind, warmhearted, and happy that everybody who saw her loved her dearly.

One day when the princess was all alone in the castle, she climbed up into an old tower she had never seen before. There

was a little door with an old rusty key. The princess, who was now fifteen years old, turned the key. There was a little room, and in it sat an old woman with a spindle, busily spinning her flax.

"Good day, little mother," said the king's daughter. "What are you doing?"

"I am spinning," replied the old woman. "Would you like to try it?"

"Oh, yes, please," said the princess, delighted.

But no sooner did she pick up the spindle than the bad wish came true and she pricked her finger with it. At once she fell into a deep sleep.

A great quiet spread over the whole castle. The king and queen, who had just come home, fell asleep in the big hall, together with all their courtiers. The horses slept in their stables, the dogs in the backyard, the doves on the roof, the flies on the walls. Even the crackling fire became still and fell asleep. The roast stopped sizzling, and the cook, who just wanted to box his boy's ear, let him fall asleep. The wind stopped blowing, and in the big trees no leaf stirred.

All around the castle a hedge of thorns started to grow. It became thicker and higher each year until finally the castle was completely hidden. One could not even see the flag on the roof any more. But all through the country people talked about the lovely princess who had fallen asleep, and they called her "Sleeping Beauty." Many a prince came and tried to get through the thorny hedge into the castle, but none succeeded. No man nor animal could get through the thick and thorny hedge.

At the end of a hundred years a handsome young prince came from far away. He had heard of the unbelievable beauty of the princess, and he wanted to cut the hedge and wake up Sleeping Beauty. People warned him not to go, but he said, "I am not afraid. I want to see Sleeping Beauty more than anything else in the world."

When he came close to the hedge, suddenly the thorns changed into beautiful flowers which parted to let him walk through. In the court of the castle he saw the horses and dogs sleeping. In the kitchen the sleeping cook still held out his hand to catch the boy, and the maid sat there with a chicken which should have been plucked one hundred years ago. The

prince saw all the ladies and gentlemen asleep and the king and queen next to their throne. Everything was so quiet that he could hear himself breathing. He went on and finally came to the tower. He opened the door to the little room in which the princess slept. There she lay and was so beautiful that he could not take his eyes from her. He bent over her and kissed her.

At the touch of the kiss the magic spell was broken. Slowly Sleeping Beauty opened her eyes and smiled up at the prince.

They went down hand in hand, and the king woke up, and the queen and all the people of the court looked at each other with big eyes. The horses in the yard got up, the dogs barked, the doves flew off the roof into the field, the flies started crawling up and down the walls again, and the fire in the kitchen woke up and crackled and cooked food once more. The roast started to sizzle. The cook boxed the kitchen boy's ear so that he screamed.

Then Sleeping Beauty and her prince were married in great splendor and lived happily ever after.

QUESTIONS

1. When the king and queen had a feast for the new princess, who was the guest that was not invited?
2. What was the gift of the uninvited guest?
3. What was the gift of the twelfth fairy?
4. How did the princess prick her finger?
5. What happened when the princess pricked her finger?
6. Why were the young princes not able to rescue the princess?
7. How was the princess finally rescued?

The Monkeys

Indian Folk Tale

Monkeys chatter all the time. At night they sit together on palm trees and sleep. When it rains the baby monkeys whine and cry because they are cold. Even the mother monkeys groan and complain. Then the father monkeys say, "Tomorrow we will build a house."

Another one says, "Yes, tomorrow for sure!"

When morning comes, the sun shines warmly, and everyone is happy again. Then one father monkey asks, "Shall we build our house now?"

"Let me eat first," answers one.

And another says, "I want to play a little bit first."

And all the others echo, "Me too! Me too!"

They eat and play all day long and forget all about building the house.

WORDS TO WATCH		
chatter	groan	build
palm trees	complain	monkeys

But during the night, it starts raining again, and again the monkeys get very cold. They think of a nice, warm house and chatter, "We have to be sure to build our house tomorrow!"

And what do you think happens the next morning? They forget about it again. And so it goes, day after day, night after night.

QUESTIONS

1. Why did the monkeys want to build a house?
2. Why didn't they build a house?
3. When you plan something, do you finish it?

The Elephant's Trunk
American Folk Rhyme

The elephant carries a great big trunk;
He never packs it with clothes;
It has no lock and it has no key,
But he takes it wherever he goes.

Animals of the Sea

I. Read and Spell

carp	shark	catfish
bass	clam	swordfish
goldfish	flying fish	salmon
trout	perch	tuna
sea horse	eel	starfish
sunfish	minnow	guppy
sucker	jellyfish	octopus

II. Read and Answer

1. Which of these is the largest? The smallest?
2. Which of these live only in salt water?
3. Which are good for pets?
4. Which of these do people like to eat?
5. Which of these can be dangerous to people?
6. Name some other kinds of fish or animals that live in the water.

III. Write

1. Write five sentences, each one telling something about a fish or animal named on this page.
2. Write a little story about one of these fish.

The Emperor's New Clothes

Hans Christian Andersen

Once there lived an emperor who was more interested in clothes than in his people. All day long he thought about new clothes. He had a coat for every hour of the day. He was so busy changing clothes that when one of his people wanted to see him, the servants would always say, "The emperor is in his dressing room."

One day two men, who were not as honest as they should have been, came to the land. They sent word to the emperor that they were weavers. "The cloth we weave is very unusual," they said. "It is entirely invisible to anyone who is silly or unfit for his job."

"This would be a fine cloth for me to have," thought the emperor. "Then I could learn much about the people who work for me. If anyone could not see my clothes, I would know that he was either silly or not fit for his job."

So he ordered the weavers to set up their looms and start making cloth for him.

The two dishonest men asked the emperor for money for the finest silk and the most expensive gold thread, but they never used the money at all. They put it in their pockets and sat there pretending that they were weaving.

After a while, the emperor thought he would go and see how the weavers were getting along with the unusual cloth they were making for him. When the emperor looked at the looms, he could see nothing, for there was nothing to see.

"Goodness me!" he thought. "Can it be that I am silly or unfit for my job? I must pretend that I can see the cloth."

"Isn't it beautiful?" said the two men who were not as honest as they should have been. "See the lovely pattern and the beautiful colors! You must admit that they are very unusual."

"Yes, yes," replied the emperor. "It is just as beautiful as you said. I shall give great honors to you weavers."

And he gave each of them a medal to wear and the title "Knight of the Loom."

"Why not have a big parade when you first wear the garments made from this wonderful cloth?" asked one of his courtiers.

"That's a splendid idea," said the emperor, who always liked to be flattered.

The night before the parade, the people saw the light of the weaving room burning all night. The weavers had stayed up all night pretending to be putting the finishing touches to the emperor's new clothes. They sewed and they sewed, but there was no need to put any thread in their needles because there was no cloth and no thread. At last they said, "Everything is ready."

One of the weavers held out the trousers to the emperor, and the other held out the coat. The emperor felt a little strange pretending to put on the trousers and the coat when he couldn't see them.

"And here is your cape," said the first weaver. The emperor pretended to put that on too.

Then the emperor started marching down the street at the head of the parade.

"Beautiful! Magnificent!" the people exclaimed as the emperor marched past them. They had all heard about the story of the unusual cloth, and they were ashamed to say that they could not see it, for no one wanted to be called silly or unfit for his job.

The emperor held his head high and felt very proud as he marched long. The two weavers laughed to themselves to think how easy it was to make people look silly.

Suddenly a little girl's voice rose above the murmurs of the crowd. "But he has nothing on!" she cried.

Soon her words reached everyone's ears, and others began to whisper and then to shout, "BUT HE HAS NOTHING ON!"

Then the foolish emperor felt very silly indeed. The people, too, began to see that they had been tricked, and they felt almost as silly as the emperor. But the little girl did not feel silly, for she had spoken the truth. Besides, she had made the people speak the truth, too.

I Had a Nickel

American Folk Rhyme

I had a nickel and I walked around the block.
I walked right into a baker shop.
I took two doughnuts right out of the grease;
I handed the lady my five-cent piece.
She looked at the nickel and she looked at me,
And said, "This money's no good to me.
There's a hole in the nickel, and it goes right through."
Said I, "There's a hole in the doughnut too."

The Riddle of the Sphinx

Greek Myth

A long, long time ago there lived a monster called the Sphinx. This Sphinx had the head of a woman, the body of a lion, and the wings of a bird.

The Sphinx lived near an old, old city named Thebes. Whenever a traveler passed by her, she would give him a riddle. If the traveler could not answer the riddle, the Sphinx would eat him up.

Here is the riddle of the Sphinx, "What walks on four legs in the morning, on two legs at noon, and three legs in the evening?"

WORDS TO WATCH		
traveler	Sphinx	Thebes
Oedipus	riddle	upright

142

Many people in Thebes were eaten by the Sphinx because they did not know the answer to the riddle. They were very much afraid of the Sphinx, and they did not know what to do.

Then one day a very clever man came along. His name was Oedipus. As he passed by the Sphinx one day, she stopped him and asked him her riddle, "What walks on four legs in the morning, on two legs at noon, and on three legs in the evening?"

"That is easy," said Oedipus. "The answer is *man,* for man crawls on all fours when he is a baby, he walks upright when he is grown, and he uses a cane when he is old."

This was the right answer. The Sphinx became so angry that she jumped off a cliff and killed herself. Now travelers could pass in safety.

The people of Thebes were so happy and grateful that they made Oedipus their king.

QUESTIONS

1. What was the riddle of the Sphinx?
2. What is the answer to the riddle?
3. Why were the people of Thebes glad when Oedipus solved the riddle?
4. How did they show Oedipus that they liked what he did?

THE GOOPS

Gelett Burgess

The Goops they lick their fingers,
    And the Goops they lick their knives;
They spill their broth on the tablecloth—
    Oh, they lead disgusting lives!
The Goops they talk while eating,
    And loud and fast they chew;
And that is why I'm glad that I
    Am not a Goop—are you?

Habits

I. Read and Remember
Good Habits

brush your teeth	go to bed on time
obey your parents	read good books
say "please" and "thank you"	have good table manners
watch out for cars	get lots of exercise
be on time	obey your teacher
study hard in school	be neat and orderly
be polite	help with chores at home
do a good deed every day	obey the laws

Bad Habits

watching too much television	daydreaming too much
eating before meals	careless speaking and writing
playing with matches	being unkind to people

II. Read and Answer
1. Why are each of these good habits important?
2. Why are each of these bad habits bad?
3. Name some other good habits and bad habits.
4. What do you think is your worst habit?

III. Write
Write a story about a good habit, and tell why it is good.

I. A. You have read these stories in Part Three of your book. Tell what each is about.

> The Boy and the Worm
>
> The Bremen Town Musicians
>
> Christmas Is Coming
>
> Why the Bear Has a Short Tail
>
> Androcles and the Lion
>
> The Milkmaid and Her Pail
>
> The Quarrel
>
> Sleeping Beauty
>
> The Monkeys
>
> The Emperor's New Clothes
>
> The Riddle of the Sphinx

B. Which of these stories do you like best? Why?

II. A. Memorize a poem you read in Part Three of your book and recite it to the class.

B. Copy the poem you like best in Part Three. Copy it carefully.

Part Four
For Readers
Brave and Bold

We're readers brave and bold;
We know that reading's fun;
So if you want to hear,
We'll show you how it's done.

The Shoemaker and the Elves

Brothers Grimm

Once upon a time there lived a shoemaker. This shoemaker was a good man, and he worked very hard, but he could not earn enough money to live on. All he had left was one piece of leather which was just enough to make one pair of shoes.

Before he went to bed that night, he cut out the leather to make the shoes, for he wanted to get up early to finish them.

He then went to bed, said his prayers, and was soon asleep, for he had nothing on his conscience to trouble him.

WORDS TO WATCH		
shoemaker	leather	conscience
examined	delighted	curtain

The next morning he awoke, said his prayers, and sat down to work. But to his great surprise, there stood the shoes upon the table already made.

The good man did not know what to say or think. He picked up the shoes, examined them closely, and saw that they were perfectly made. They were neat and shiny, and there was not a single bad stitch in them.

That same day a customer saw the shoes in the shop window. He was so delighted with these shoes that he paid the shoemaker a high price for them.

With this money the shoemaker bought enough leather for two more pairs of shoes. That night he cut out the leather with the idea of getting up early in the morning to finish the shoes.

He went to bed as usual. When he awoke the next morning, there on the table he found two more pairs of shoes, as perfectly made as the first pair.

And so it went. Every time the shoemaker cut out the leather for a pair of shoes, he found next morning that someone had made a perfect pair of shoes for him.

One evening at Christmas time, the shoemaker and his wife were sitting before the fire, and the shoemaker said, "I would like to sit up tonight and watch to see who makes the shoes for me every night."

"I will watch with you," said the shoemaker's wife.

And so the shoemaker and his wife hid behind the curtain that night. Just as the clock struck twelve, they saw something so strange that they could hardly believe their eyes. Two little elves came into the workshop, climbed upon the table, and began to work on the shoes. Their nimble fingers tapped with the hammer and stitched with the needle. They worked so fast and so well that soon the shoes were finished and ready for someone to wear. Then, in a twinkling, they were gone.

After the wife had time to catch her breath, she said to the shoemaker, "Did you see how poorly dressed those little elves are? They had nothing on their backs but rags, and they were shivering from the cold. Those little elves have made us rich, and I am going to help them. Tomorrow I will make new shirts and trousers for them and good heavy coats besides."

"And did you see that they were barefoot?" replied the shoemaker. "I will make them some new shoes."

The next day the shoemaker and his wife made new clothes and shoes for the little elves and put them on the work table. That night they hid behind the curtain again, and at midnight the elves came in as usual.

When they saw the clothes lying on the table, they laughed and jumped about with glee. They put on the new clothes and saw that they fit perfectly. Then they sang merrily and danced about until they danced right out the door and over the hill.

The shoemaker and his wife never saw the little elves again, but they were very happy, and everything went well with them as long as they lived.

QUESTIONS

1. How were the elves helping the shoemaker?
2. What did the shoemaker's wife do to help the elves?
3. What did the shoemaker do to help them?
4. Why did the shoemaker and his wife hide behind the curtain the first time?
5. Why did they hide behind it the second time?

Good, Better, Best

Anonymous

Good, better, best.
Never rest
Till "good" is "better,"
And "better," "best."

The Table
and the Chair

Edward Lear

Said the Table to the Chair,
"You can hardly be aware
How I suffer from the heat
And from chilblains on my feet.
If we took a little walk,
We might have a little talk;
Pray let us take the air,"
Said the Table to the Chair.

Said the Chair unto the Table,
"Now you know we are not able.
How foolishly you talk,
When you know we cannot walk!"
Said the Table with a sigh,
"It can do no harm to try.
I've as many legs as you.
Why can't we walk on two?"

So they both went slowly down,
And walked about the town
With a cheerful bumpy sound
As they toddled round and round;
And everybody cried,
As they hastened to their side,
"See! The Table and the Chair
Have come out to take the air!"

But in going down an alley
To a castle in a valley,
They completely lost their way,
And wandered all the day;
Till, to see them safely back,
They paid a Ducky-quack,
And a Beetle, and a Mouse,
Who took them to their house.

Then they whispered to each other,
"Oh, delightful little brother,
What a lovely walk we've taken!
Let us dine on beans and bacon."
So the Ducky and the leetle
Browny-Mousy and the Beetle
Dined and danced upon their heads
Till they toddled to their beds.

Scrambled Words

I. Unscramble

yob	eder	arhci	dnowwi
yda	rigl	srohe	arechet
gpi	ogod	uoseh	prsots
nma	ribd	rewat	lhosco
yee	ersto	roflo	tehmor
ylf	nosw	rheat	epnicl
ary	toba	tanip	klena

II. Read and Answer

1. Find another word that the letters in each of these words make:

rat	pool	peek	state
art	pest	leap	meat

2. See how many words you can make out of the letters in this word:

a u t o m o b i l e

More than thirty words are possible.

I Saw a Ship A-Sailing

Mother Goose

I saw a ship a-sailing,
    A-sailing on the sea,
And, oh, it was all laden
    With pretty things for me.

There were comfits in the cabin,
    And apples in the hold;
The sails were made of silk,
    And the masts were all of gold.

The four-and-twenty sailors,
    That stood between the decks,
Were four-and-twenty white mice
    With chains about their necks.

The captain was a duck
    With a packet on his back,
And when the ship began to move,
    The captain said, "Quack! Quack!"

A Birthday Surprise

Arther S. Trace, Jr.

"I know something very special," Dad said, and smiled at Mom as if he had a secret.

"Am I going to get an electric train?" asked Tom.

"I know something very special about your birthday," Dad said.

"Am I going to get a new baseball mitt?" asked Tom.

"Tom, you are going to get something special for your birthday."

Finally his birthday came. Tom didn't get any of the things that he had thought about. Instead, on the table was a high round bowl. It was filled with water and green plants that had

---

WORDS TO WATCH

feelers	flutters	greenish
bluish	tadpoles	scummy
reddish	breeding	earthworms

feathery leaves. Between the leaves Tom saw little black animals with small bodies and little wiggling tails. Then he saw two water snails. What a funny round house they carried around with them! Tom watched their long thin feelers and their mouths that opened and closed.

"What are they doing?" Tom asked his Dad.

"Those are your street cleaners. They eat everything to keep your bowl neat and clean."

"And those little animals with the tails, Dad, what are they?"

"That is what is so special. It is a riddle for you. Look at them closely, and you will see that they are very young, fresh from the eggs. Very slowly they will change into something different."

"They must be little birds," called Tom's little sister Cathy.

"Oh, no," said Tom, "I think they are little fish."

Dad laughed and said, "Many animals come from eggs and are not birds or fish. Look how fast they swim!"

Cathy went to the bowl for another look. "Now I know," she called. "They are mice. That tail is like a baby mouse tail."

No, they were not mice. They were not birds. They were not fish. But what were they? The children waited and watched each day, and each day they saw something new.

"Look, they have black eyes. I see how they are drinking. Then they go to the plants where the leaves are brown. They are nibbling." And one day, "Oh, Dad, their eyes are not black. They are gold. And the animals are not black any more. They are bluish and reddish with bright spots." The children kept watching day by day.

"They are playing with each other. That big one always comes up to the others. Then they lean their heads on each other. The little tail flutters like a flag in the wind." Then one day Tom got very excited and called his Dad.

"Look! Look! Next to his tail the biggest one has legs —new legs that were not there before. I can see them." A few days later they were all like this. They all had real legs with a real knee and foot. But what animal has two legs and a tail? Then they got fatter and fatter and fatter.

Then one morning something very special was there. Two little arms had grown out of the fat part up front. Now they had four feet with a tail.

Now Tom knew. "Dad, now I know what they are. They are little frogs, and before they were tadpoles."

"Yes," Dad said. "We have been breeding frogs. Each one starts out as an egg. Then it turns into something like a fish but is not a real fish. Then it grows up and has legs and lungs. At first it could live in water like a fish. Now it can live in the air just as we do. We must put the frogs out in the fresh air. Look!"

Dad put a small board on the water. One by one the little frogs climbed up on it. The children saw how their little chests moved up and down. The frogs were breathing through their lungs. The children watched for several days until the tails shrank back and disappeared.

Then one day Tom asked his friend, "What are you doing after school, John?"

"I'm going to play baseball. Want to come along?"

Tom said, "No, but why don't you come with me? I know something special. We are going to the pond to put out our frogs. They are big enough and strong enough to go worm hunting on their own now. When they were still small, their food was stored in their tails. When they were growing, they needed that greenish scummy stuff that we found on the edge of the pond. Then when their tails were almost gone, I began to feed them earthworms, soft insects, flies, grasshoppers, and crickets. But now they are big and should be outside. Come along with me."

QUESTIONS

1. Why was this present a real birthday surprise?
2. Find out as much about tadpoles and frogs as you can and tell your class what you have learned.

The Crocodile

Lewis Carroll

How doth the little crocodile
　　Improve his shining tail,
And pour the waters of the Nile
　　On every golden scale!

How cheerfully he seems to grin,
　　How neatly spreads his claws,
And welcomes little fishes in,
　　With gently smiling jaws!

Part Five
On Your Own

SAM

Ann Herbert Scott

Sam wanted to play.
Everyone in his house was busy, and no one wanted to play
with him.

Sam walked into the kitchen, where his mother was peeling apples for pie. He picked up a knife from the table.

"SAM, don't touch that knife," cried his mother. "That knife is very sharp—too sharp for little boys. I don't ever want to see you touch that knife again."

Sam's mother went back to peeling apples. "Why don't you go outside and play, Sammy," she said.

Sam walked out on the porch. His big brother George was sitting on the steps, reading his books from school.

Sam picked up a book and turned the pages to find a picture.

"SAM, put down that book," yelled George. "That's *my* book, and you're not to touch it."

Sam looked as if he might cry.

"That's a book I got from school," said George, not quite so loud as before. "If you get it dirty or rip the pages, I'll be in trouble. Don't ever touch my books again. Understand?"

Sam just stood there.

"Why don't you go inside and play, Sammy," said George.

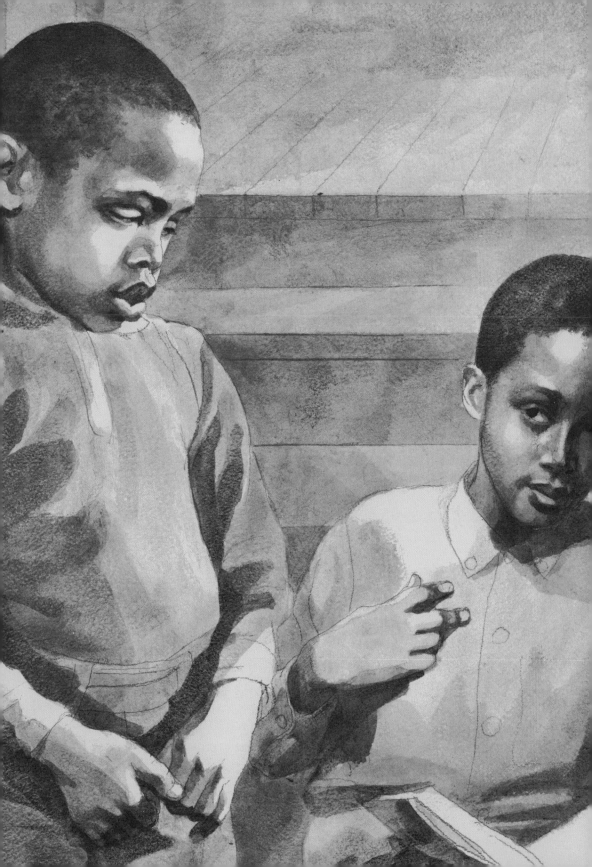

Sam went into the living room. There by the window his big sister Marcia was making clothes for her paper dolls.

Sam picked up one of the dolls and waved its hand up and down.

"SAM," screamed Marcia when she saw what he was doing. "You'll bend my doll's hand. You'll *ruin* her!"

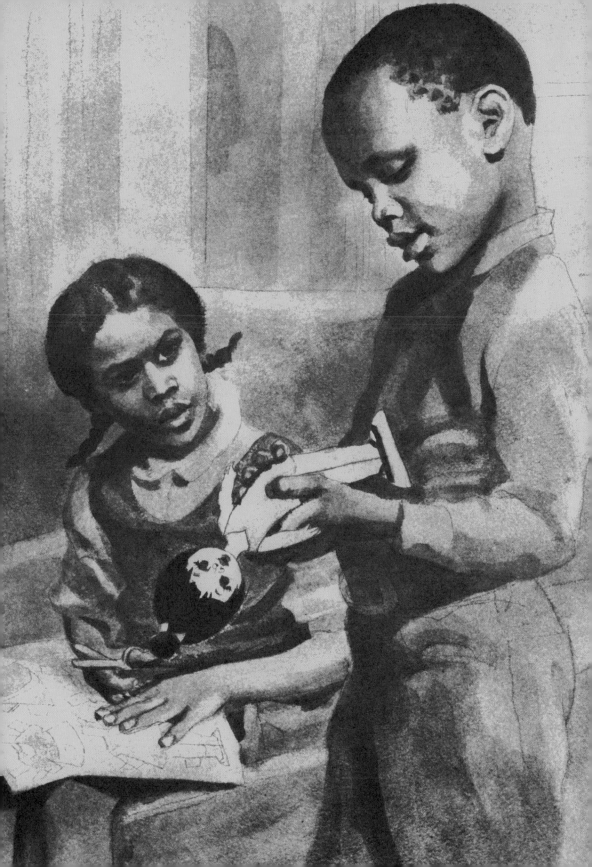

Sam looked as if he might cry.

"You go play somewhere else, Sammy. But don't ever touch my dolls again."

Sam just stood there.

"Why don't you go find Daddy," said Marcia.

Sam's father was sitting at his desk, reading the newspaper. Sam stood beside him for a minute. Then PING, Sam punched down a key on the typewriter.

"SAM, get your hands off that typewriter," shouted his father. "How many times must I tell you—that typewriter is not a toy for children. Typewriters are very easy to break and they cost lots of money to fix. Don't ever touch my typewriter again."

Sam's father turned back to his newspaper. "Why don't you go find Mother," he said.

Then Sam really did cry. He sat right down on the floor by his father's desk and he cried and cried and cried.

He cried so loud that his mother came in from the kitchen and his big brother George came in from the porch and his big sister Marcia came in from the living room.

"What in the world is the matter with Sam?" asked his father.

"I think I know," said his mother, sitting down in the rocking chair by the desk and picking up Sam in her arms.

"I think I know, too," said George.

"I think I know, too," said Marcia.

For a minute everyone was quiet. The rocking chair
creaked back and forth as Sam curled in his mother's arms.

"Sammy," said his mother, "if you're not too busy, there's
a job you could do for me in the kitchen."

Sam was tired of crying, so he followed his mother into the
kitchen. His father and his big sister and his big brother all
came along, too.

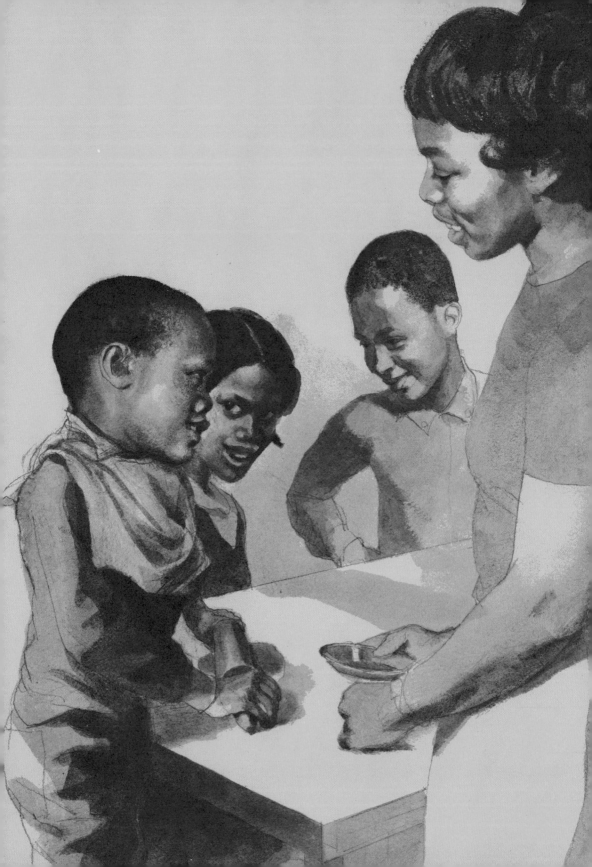

Sam's mother pulled out a tall kitchen stool so he could reach the table. Then she pinned a dish towel around his neck so he wouldn't get dirty. And then she gave him a piece of soft pie dough and a rolling pin so he could roll the dough out flat.

"There's just enough dough to fit in this little pan," said Sam's mother. "Maybe you can make a tart to bake in the oven with the pie."

"Say, that's a good job for Sam," said his father.

"He's not too little," said his sister.

"And he's not too big," said his brother.

"In fact," said his mother, "he's just the right size. And now, Sammy, what kind of jam would you like for your tart?"

"Raspberry," said Sam.